THE BARN OWL

HAMLYN SPECIES GUIDES

THE BARN OWL

Colin Shawyer

HAMLYN

To my Father

First published in 1994 by Hamlyn Limited,
an imprint of Reed Consumer Books Ltd
Michelin House, 81 Fulham Road, London SW3 6RB
and Auckland, Melbourne, Singapore and Toronto

ISBN 0 600 57949 2

A CIP catalogue record for this book is available from the British Library

Page design by Jessica Caws
Maps on pages 11 and 27 drawn by Louise Griffiths
Printed in Hong Kong

CONTENTS

	Series Editor's Foreword	7
	Preface and Acknowledgements	8
	Introduction	10
1	DESCRIPTION	12
2	HISTORY	21
3	DISTRIBUTION	26
4	HABITAT	35
5	FOOD AND FEEDING	43
6	TERRITORY AND TERRITORIAL BEHAVIOUR	58
7	VOICE	61
8	SOCIAL BEHAVIOUR AND DISPLAYS	64
9	BREEDING	67
10	MOULT	88
11	MOVEMENTS	91
12	LIFESPAN AND LONGEVITY	92
13	MORTALITY AND CAUSES OF DECLINE	94
14	CONSERVATION	115
	Select Bibliography	124
	Scientific Names of Species	126
	Index	127

Hilary Burn

Series Editor's Foreword

In the early 1960s, during my adolescence, I would take great pleasure in watching the many Barn Owls hunting at dusk and into the early night over what were then extensive rough grasslands near my home in south Hampshire. On countless summer evenings I lay on my back and marvelled at the ghostly shapes moving silently by, or sat motionless watching them quartering a favoured piece of ground in their hunt for small mammals to take back to their nests in the old barns and derelict buildings that were such a feature of the landscape of the time. This was a truly magical and mysterious bird, awe-inspiring in a genuine way.

One of the delights of birdwatching is that one can simply sit and watch nature, admire its many facets and wonders, and learn so much about and it relates to our own existence. The Barn Owl in those early days confirmed and reinforced my belief in our duty to protect all wildlife and all wild habitats.

Since that time, however, with an ever-increasing human population, an unprecedented growth in use of the motor car and associated road-building schemes, intensification of agriculture and farming methods accompanied by a frequently uncontrolled use of toxic pesticides, and in too many cases a total disregard for the needs of wildlife, the countryside has, in a period of just thirty years, changed beyond all recognition. This has been particularly marked in Britain, where many bird (and other) species now have to make do with much-reduced areas of suitable habitat. While 'new' habitats have sometimes been created to compensate in part for the losses, these have often been of limited benefit and far from adequate. For the Barn Owl, with its highly specialized ecological requirements, the problems have been, and in most areas remain, acute.

As Colin Shawyer so profoundly demonstrates in his text here, this unique owl which screams, snores, hisses and clicks, but does not hoot, merits special attention from conservationists. Anybody who has ever spent any time watching this wonderful owl will delight in learning about the many sides of its life described and explained in this book – such as its astounding capacity, when all necessary conditions are satisfied, to recover from major setbacks.

The Barn Owl is a beautiful bird and positively beneficial to man. The importance of ensuring that man does not, through his ignorance and short-sightedness, drive it from our countryside for ever cannot be overstated. With the appropriate and informed attitude that comes from objective studies, we can achieve this aim, as Colin Shawyer's book shows.

David A. Christie

Preface

The Barn Owl is an astonishingly beautiful bird, and the spiritual vision of 'old hushwing' drifting in dreamy silence over a misty meadow is a treasure which it is impossible to price or enumerate. Although ghostly pale in the moonlight, in reality its plumage is sprinkled with tiny white teardrops which cascade over golden powder-puff feathers washed with steel-blue silver. Floating like a tissue on a breeze, the White Owl appears at the will of the wind and there is no other bird which possesses such buoyant aerial grace. The dreamy ease with which its delicate white body rises and falls with each wingbeat belies its manoeuvrability as it stalls, hovers and cartwheels into the grass after some unsuspecting vole.

This is a bird resolutely faithful to lonely farmsteads and forgotten habitats, and 'old hushwing', once steeped in superstition and feared for its silent flight and chilling call, remains shrouded in mystery. Helped by Neolithic peoples who cleared the land of forest, and later by the provision of owl windows in barns, this symbiotic relationship with man has endured back into the very depths of time. Fiercely and jealously protected by some farmers today, the Barn Owl is justifiably *their* bird, a powerful natural indicator of the effects of habitat destruction, pesticides and pollution and a flagship for conservation aspirations.

Unfortunately, our precious remnant population is by no means secure in our modern countryside, which has been raped of its secret unspoiled places, once found in our meadowlands and hidden alongside rivers and streams where this owl coasted beneath the moon. Today, farmers, because of the overproduction of food, have been told that they must convert their hard-won lands into temporary fields of deserted land which not only destroy their soul but are of little use as permanent habitats for the fragile species we are trying to conserve. Management of wild flora and fauna is not so different from the management of crops or domestic livestock, but until we provide farmers with the satisfaction of creating something positive from their unfarmed lands both they and treasures like the Barn Owl are unlikely to prosper.

Acknowledgements

Firstly, I should like to thank my family, especially my wife, Val, who has slaved over processing the many drafts of this manuscript, and my children, Emilie and Matthew, who during the course of writing this book have put up with my tantrums and neglect. Special thanks are due to The Hawk and Owl Trust, particularly Paul Johnson, Chris Sperring and Jack Orchel, and to the Institute of Terrestrial Ecology at Monks Wood, especially Ian Newton and Ian Wyllie, who have always made me so welcome on my many visits there. Likewise to Humphrey Crick, David Glue and others at the BTO for their interest and assistance. I am deeply grateful to all the photographers listed, many of whom are close friends, for so generously providing the photographs which grace these pages. My studies would not have been possible without the help of scores of Barn Owl researchers and enthusiasts who have always been so loyal in their support since 1982 when I first conducted the Barn Owl Survey of Britain and Ireland and who have enriched my understanding of this species over the years.

INTRODUCTION

There are about 133 different species of owl in the world, classified in the order Strigiformes, which is divided into two main families, Tytonidae and Strigidae, each of which has two subfamilies. Tytonidae contains the Tytoninae, with the single genus, *Tyto* (barn and grass owls), and the Phodilinae, with the single genus *Phodilus* (bay owls). The Strigidae, however, has 24 different genera divided between two sub-families, the Buboninae and the Striginae. Both main families have many features in common: very soft plumage, eyes directed forward, bills hooked and facing downwards, and the cere at the base of the bill bristle-covered. The outer toe can be placed forward or backward and, unlike Falconiformes, owls have no crop. The Tytonidae, unlike the Strigidae, have a heart-shaped face, the tail often ending in a shallow 'V' and inner and middle toes of equal length with the claw or talon of the middle toe with a comb-like serrated edge. The wishbone and breastbone are fused and the bone dividing the eye sockets is thick. The eyes are dark, the relatively small ear openings long, with a small orifice covered by a large flap. The rounded wings are large, with long, similar-length eighth, ninth and tenth primary feathers. The legs are long and slender, and the mesoptile plumage of the young (the second plumage, acquired in the nest) is downy and unlike true feathers. There are other differences, but these are too detailed for this book.

The bay owls are represented by two species, and the barn owls by ten or eleven (the Sula Islands Barn Owl may be extinct). The nominate Barn Owl *Tyto alba*, has been separated into 35 subspecies (or races) and is found in every continent except Antarctica, with four races in Europe, seven in Africa and the Middle East, eleven in south and east Asia and Australia and thirteen in North and South America. The Barn Owl is therefore considered the most widely distributed landbird in the world, occurring in most of Europe (except Fennoscandia and Malta), most of Africa (except the Sahara), India, Pakistan, south-east Asia and Australia through the Pacific Islands and to North, Central and South America. It is therefore found in widely differing zones ranging from the extremes of tropical rainforest to desert climates, although these two extremes are usually avoided.

The Barn Owl does not, however, breed in China, Mongolia, Korea, Japan, Taiwan, Borneo, the Philippines or the Moluccas, nor in Iran, Afghanistan, the neighbouring countries of the CIS to the south and in all but the extreme west of Russia. It is also absent from Greenland, Iceland and all but the southern fringes of Canada and, in the southern hemisphere, from Antarctica and New Zealand although odd stragglers have turned up here on occasions, which demonstrates the species' ability to cross large expanses of water. The northern limit of the Barn Owl's breeding range is at about 58 °N in the north of Scotland (Shawyer 1987), and in the southern hemisphere the species does not extend this far from the equator. The different races vary in size from the tiny Barn Owl of the

Fig 1 *World distribution of the Barn Owl* Tyto alba.

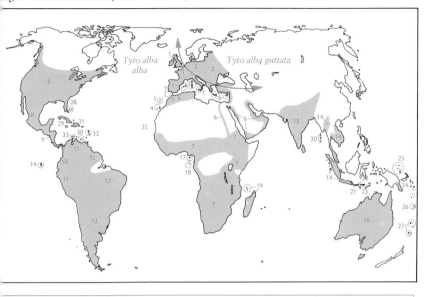

Key

	12 T.a. hellmayri; **13** T.a. tuidara;	**24** T.a. meeki; **25** T.a. crassirostris;
T.a. alba; **2** T.a. guttata; **3** T.a. ernesti;	**14** T.a. javanica; **15** T.a. stertens;	**26** T.a. interposita; **27** T.a. lulu;
T.a. gracilirostris; **5** T.a. schmitzi;	**16** T.a. deliculata; **17** T.a. poensis;	**28** T.a. lucayana; **29** T.a. furcata;
T.a. erlangeri; **7** T.a. affinis;	**18** T.a. thomensis; **19** T.a. hypermetra;	**30** T.a. glaucops; **31** T.a. nigrescens;
T.a. pratincola; **9** T.a. guatemalae;	**20** T.a. de-roepstorffi; **21** T.a. sumbënsis;	**32** T.a. insularis; **33** T.a. bargei;
0 T.a. subandeana; **11** T.a. contempta,	**22** T.a. everetti; **23** T.a. kuehni;	**34** T.a. punctatissima; **35** T.a. detorta.

eastern Canary Isles (*T.a. gracilirostris*), measuring only 28 cm, to the much larger race (*T. a furcata*), in Cuba, which is 43 cm (Voous 1988).

The Barn Owl is mainly a bird of open habitats: grassland, wetland, semi-arid areas and savanna, but is also able to exploit grassy margins in some of the most intensively farmed and afforested regions of the world as well as inside mature oil palm, date and coconut plantations where trees are well spaced and flight is unhindered.

The name Barn Owl seems to have first appeared in 1678, in John Day's translation of Francis Willughby's *Ornithology* from Latin. Thomas Pennant, in 1766, referred in *The British Zoology*, to the 'White Owl', and William Yarrel in his *History of British Birds* in 1843 to the 'White or Barn Owl'. Christopher Merrett in his 1666 list of British birds had referred to the Barn Owl as the 'Screech Owl', 'Scrich Owl' or 'Scritch Owl' although this name was also used to refer to the Tawny Owl. *Tyto* is a Greek word derived from the Latin *Tuto* (meaning owl), and *alba* is Latin for white. The Barn Owl's long and close association with rural life and man's obvious fascination for the bird, led to a vast selection of evocative county names in Britain, some of which are still in use today. My particular favourites are Old Hushwing, Billy Wix, Cherubim or Church Owl, Jenny Howlet, Gill Houter, Hoolet, Woolert, Povey and Pudge, and many other derivatives.

11

1

DESCRIPTION

At close quarters, the plumage of the Barn Owl is incredibly beautiful. Viewed from beneath it appears almost pure white, although some birds have a distinct yellow orange or buff suffusion in a wide band around the chest (sometimes restricted to the sides of the breast). This often quite subtle coloration is particularly noticeable on juvenile birds, especially young females, on which it can extend over a large part of the underbody on occasions. This colour, which seems to be present at the tips of these downy feathers, appears to lighten even before the first moult begins, perhaps as a result of the feathers becoming minutely abraded at their ends during preening, for example, or simply because they fade in the light. After the moult, however, this breast tinge becomes noticeably paler and males often lose it altogether. Most females also have spotting on the breast, flanks, legs and underwing which can vary from tiny black flecks to larger grey or grey-brown droplets. Female birds usually possess much more silvery or blue-grey feathering than males, particularly on the wing-coverts, and this can become the dominant colour on some individuals. The head and back are golden-buff, with individual feathers on the head, wing-coverts and back having a small elongated white and black eye fleck or droplet. These delicate flecks and markings are arranged in rows up and down the back, which probably help to break up the bird's outline and provide some form of camouflage.

The wings of the Barn Owl are broad, long and rounded, providing enormous lift, great manoeuvrability and controlled slow wavering flight when hunting low to the ground. My own measurements of live birds give wing length usually of 285–298 mm, with only minor differences between the sexes. There are ten main primary wing feathers with a short grey-white rudimentary one situated out of sequence above the shaft of the second main primary hidden under the coverts, and fourteen secondary wing feathers. On their upper surfaces these feathers are golden-buff along the outer webs (sometimes speckled grey), the colour extending across the shaft for a small distance into the inner web; the main part of which is silky-white possessing the silvery velvet pile so characteristic of Barn Owl feathers. Across the golden-buff coloration run four to six transverse bars, which vary in shape from small circles to wide chevrons and in colour from pale grey through to dark brown or black. At the feather tips, the golden-buff usually merges into grey. For 2.5 cm or so towards the feather's end the barbules on both webs change to pure white, and at the base these are very soft, loose and downy in appearance. The outer main primary feather, number 10, has a slender outer web and is more pointed than the rest. Along its leading edge it has a fine comb-like fringe about

1 mm wide made up of stiff hair-like extensions on the end of each individual barbule. This fringe, together with the velvety pile on the undersides of the main wing feathers, is believed to moderate the passage of air over the wing surface, thereby minimizing noise when in flight.

The barring on the wings and tail is usually more obvious on females, but, because the coloration tends to fade with successive moults, older females sometimes appear whiter than younger males. Older males, on the other hand, can appear almost completely white on the back and across the tops of the wings, sometimes losing their barring altogether on some feathers.

The twelve tail feathers or rectrices are also golden-buff, becoming grey near their ends, with a series of four to six dark bars. The central pair is usually darkest, with both inner and outer webs evenly marked. The outer tail feathers are paler on their inner webs, becoming progressively whiter with fainter bars from the middle pairs to the outer pairs, which are sometimes pure white.

Barn Owls are noted for their well-developed facial discs. These are essentially two concave discs of short stiff feathers which are thought to funnel sound waves into the ear drum, much the same as when we cup our hands behind our own ear flaps. The discs can vary in shape from a full circle to a narrowed heart shape, which is particularly obvious when the bird is dozing so that the eyes are sunk deep within the feathers. The facial disc is surrounded by a distinct ruff of short white feathers, often tinged with brown at their tips, particularly near the chin. Again, the darker surrounds are usually associated with female birds.

Before leaving the subject of plumage, it is often asked why Barn Owls are not better camouflaged. For the answer we need look no further than the picture overleaf. Although man-made bricks have not been around very long, it is not hard to imagine that the owl would be well disguised in its original home in rock outcrops of sandstone or chalk and crevices made up of other rock forms. For a bird which lives during the day in dark cavities, disguise becomes important only when out hunting, especially when this is conducted by day. Anyone who looks down from a high vantage point on Barn Owls quartering low over rough grassland will soon understand why they are coloured as they are. They blend so completely with the pale golden stems of their favoured grasslands that it becomes almost impossible to follow their movements. Since they fly so low over open ground, the most likely form of aerial attack would come from above, and it is at such times that this remarkable camouflage would come into its own.

Hard parts

The bill, which is directed downwards, more so than in other owls, is quite slender, ivory-coloured and slightly pink around the edges. The fleshy pink cere at the base of the beak is protected by bristle-like feathers which extend into the inner corners of the eye sockets, where they become a rusty purplish-red in colour. The white legs, which are densely feathered, are especially long and dangle noticeably in flight, allowing the Barn Owl to reach deep into rank vegetation to seize prey. The feathers become progres-

ABOVE *Barn Owls were probably well camouflaged in their original homes among sandstone, chalk and other rocky outcrops.*

BELOW *Female birds are usually darker with more silvery grey on the upperwings and tail (left). Male birds can be considerably lighter and some have almost pure white primaries and secondaries (right).*

sively shorter towards the toes, which are slender, bare or lightly bristled, and vary from grey-brown to yellow; the long needle sharp claws are dark grey. The inner and middle toes are of similar length, the claws on the latter having either a thin flange or a horny comb-like structure on the innermost side, the degree of development seemingly dependent on the bird's age. The outer toe can be manoeuvred backwards but at rest sticks out to the front side of the foot. The soft pads of the feet (papillae) have tiny raised scales which help to provide a firm non-slip grip, the effectiveness of which can readily be seen when watching Barn Owls capturing slimy frogs from the edges of the mating pools in spring.

Ears

Like most owls, the Barn Owl has quite large ear openings (although much smaller than those of the Tawny, Short-eared and Long-eared Owls), located beneath the edges of the facial disc, which give it especially acute hearing. It also has adapted by having manoeuvrable ear flaps with the left one set permanently above the level of the right. This asymmetrical arrangement means that the sounds arrive at each ear at slightly different times and certain frequencies arrive at different intensities. It is thought that the owl moves its head so that the sound intensity is the same in both

The Barn Owl hunts primarily by sound. Its ear openings are hidden under the facial disc.

ABOVE *At rest, the Barn Owl's outer tow sticks out to the side of the foot* (left). *The talon flange on the middle toe is smooth when it first develops, but becomes progressively comb-like with increasing age* (right).

RIGHT *The Barn Owl's binocular vision enables it to judge distance.*

ears, so that it ends up facing the source of the sound. The hearing is so sensitive that the Barn Owl is able to locate prey in complete darkness rustling or calling beneath vegetation. It is also soon alerted to the sound of anyone approaching the roost or nest even at a considerable distance.

Eyes

The Barn Owl has small button-black eyes, in contrast to the large yellow and orange eyes of many other species of owl. In fact the iris is dark hazel, although this is not obvious from a distance. The Barn Owl has binocular vision, enabling it to judge distances accurately when hunting prey. Its eyes are fixed in their sockets with a bony vine and are unable to move and,r with a limited visual field of about 110 degrees, is not well suited to keeping an all-round watch for potential enemies. This is however over-come by the great mobility of the neck, which can turn the head through 180 degrees in each direction in the horizontal plane and 90 degrees in the vertical plane. The Barn Owl will sway its head from side to side when trying to judge the distance of an object, whereas the Little Owl does this by rapid up-and-down head-bobbing. The transparent and delicate nictitating membrane, or third eyelid, which all bird species possess, is opaque and more robust in owls, and its action of sweeping clean the front of the eye is much slower and more deliberate than in other groups. The membrane is usually drawn across the eyes when the owl is engaged in anything hazardous, such as striking at prey, preening or feeding young; at such times owls use the bristles around the bill to judge what they are doing.

While the night vision of Barn Owls is undoubtedly good, I have found when watching these birds at dusk, that they will on occasions fly to a post alongside me, once even resting on my shoulder! It seems likely therefore that, while they are capable of seeing the silhouetted obstacles of the night such as stationary trees, posts or buildings, they are less able to discern the detail of these shapes, their sensitivity to light being at the expense of good colour vision and the ability to discern detail. Their eyes are packed with cells known as rods, which are highly sensitive to low light intensity but not to colour. The eye has an especially large cornea and lens to allow the maximum of light to enter and fall on the retina. The lower numbers of colour-sensitive cells – cones – on the retina suggest that the owls may have poor colour vision; this would also indicate that they possess poorer visual resolution than diurnal birds, and that they would be less capable of locating and catching food if they were to rely on their vision alone.

Measurements

An adult Barn Owl is some 330–350 mm from head to tail, with a wing-span of 850–930 mm (Cramp 1985). There is usually only a slight size difference between the sexes, unlike many diurnal birds of prey, where the female is often larger, but weight does differ somewhat (*see* below).

The Short-eared and Long-eared Owls also hunt over open ground and are of similar size. Both are distinguished by striped underparts, large yellow or orange eyes, well-feathered toes and legs, and darker facial discs. In flight, although they can appear quite pale, particularly the Short-eared, both can be recognized by the large, obvious dark patch near the bend of the underwing. Their hunting flight is more positive and less wavering than the Barn Owl's, although the Long-eared, which is less commonly out during the day, has a buoyant and very graceful flight and is quite capable of hovering near the ground for quite long periods – just like the Barn Owl.

Body weight

During most of the year, male and female Barn Owls show very little difference in body weight, unlike many birds of prey, where the female is commonly larger and heavier. Female owls, however, can be almost 30 per cent heavier than males in the spring, when they accumulate substantial body reserves in preparation for breeding. Figure 2 shows the fluctuations in body weight of Barn Owls through the year and the differences between the sexes. This histogram was produced from the weights of specimens submitted for postmortem examination and to taxidermists when weight and sex were recorded and the cause of death was known. The samples include 165 female and 183 male Barn Owls submitted between 1982 and 1990 which died in circumstances suggesting that they were healthy

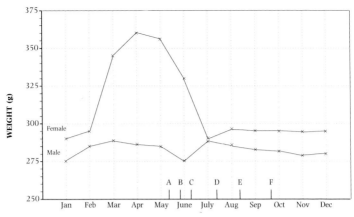

Notes: A – mean mid egg-laying date; B – incubation and beginning of moult; C – mean mid hatch; D – continuous brooding ceases; E – mean fledging date; and F – young become independent

Fig. 2 *Body weight of 348 road casualties, by sex and by month. Males show no significant change in body weight while females accumulate reserves early in the year in preparation for breeding and moult.*

immediately before death, usually as a result of collisions. During this eight-year period, only four females were found dead in May, probably because this is the normal time of egg-laying and incubation. For this reason the weight recorded for females during this month may not reflect the true average. Since most birds were likely to have been hunting immediately before being killed, with relatively empty stomachs, it is probable that the recorded body weights would be less than for live birds captured at the roost or nest. Using the mean monthly weights, average annual weights for these casualties were 285 g for males and 317 g for females, but I have recorded average annual weights of 315 g and 356 g respectively in a sample of eight male and ten female rehabilitated wild Barn Owls weighed monthly, four hours after feeding. This suggests that the dead weight may be 30–35 g lower than that of live birds. Whatever the absolute weights, the histogram does, however, provide a good indication that males maintain constant weight throughout the year, dropping slightly in June and July when the food demands of the young are greatest, while females undergo major changes during the late winter and spring months as their weight increases steadily in preparation for egg-laying, incubation and moult.

Many birds in temperate regions increase their body weight in winter to maintain insulation and provide the additional energies necessary to cope with the increased difficulties of finding food. The Tawny Owl, for example, is no exception. Both sexes achieve their maximum fat reserves and body weight between December and March, during the most severe winter months. The body weight of Barn Owls, on the other hand, is lower in winter than in spring and summer, and they appear unable to put on the reserves necessary for providing insulation and the extra energy demands needed for hunting at this difficult time of the year. Fat reserves are less important in tropical and subtropical climes where the Barn Owl is thought to have originated and where it is far more common, but in more northerly latitudes this species becomes particularly vulnerable to winter food shortages. Postmortem examinations carried out at the Institute of Terrestrial Ecology by Ian Newton and Ian Wyllie showed that Barn Owls died of starvation when female body weight fell below 250 g and male weight below 240 g, which is in both cases 25 per cent below normal live winter weight, a figure similar to the 21 per cent reported for the central European race, *T.a. guttata* (Piechocki 1960). I have found a number of freshly killed road-casualties in the phenomenally low range of 175–200 g which were presumably hunting just before being killed, but these birds probably fell at the low end of the normal weight range.

Because Tawny Owls accumulate their fat during early winter, they are not only able to survive better but are particularly efficient because, if winters are mild and hunting can be maintained, they are ready to lay eggs by March when their reserves are still high. Barn Owls, however, which are at their lowest weights in winter, are not only at risk from hypothermia and starvation, but by the end of February, which is usually the most severe winter month, the female needs to increase body weight in order to breed. The seasonal variations exhibited by these two species of owl help us to understand major differences in their ecology and the particular difficulties the Barn Owl faces in the northern parts of its range.

Sexing and ageing

Only when light conditions are good is it possible to sex an individual in the field. Females are usually recognized by the greater extent of black spotting or larger grey-brown flecking on the underwing and flanks, and first-year birds often exhibit a noticeable yellow buff collar beneath the throat. There can, however, be considerable overlap in plumage, with about one-fifth of males demonstrating spotting on some occasions and even a very light buff wash, both of which are, as I have said, more characteristic of females. When the pair is seen together then sexing is often easier, with females appearing slightly more stocky and almost always darker on the back and tops of the wings, with more flecks or spots on the underside. With males, the white breast commonly extends up around the neck as a broad white collar which stops short towards the nape, and this, in combination with the other subtle plumage differences, is usually diagnostic. Much regional variation nevertheless occurs. On the Isle of Wight, for example, some females have a very pronounced deep buff band across the chest which is much darker than I have observed on any individuals elsewhere in Britain or Ireland, although nothing like that of the dark-breasted race *T.a. guttata*, in which the whole breast is yellowy orange with heavy spotting and the face darker. Recently, a juvenile male which was very white and had no spotting underneath at all produced extensive spotting on its flanks and breast after its first moult (Pearce 1992). While this seems very unusual, it does show that even the best-laid plans for sex identification of Barn Owls can sometimes be confounded.

Unlike other species such as gulls and some diurnal birds of prey which have a distinct juvenile plumage during their first few years, Barn Owls are difficult to age in the field once they have left the nest, by which time they have already assumed adult plumage. In the hand ageing can be easier: Barn Owls have a primary moult pattern which takes three years to complete, and it is often possible, by spreading the wing and viewing the top surface, to distinguish which feathers were replaced at the last moult. In diffuse or angled light, these are often glossier, cleaner and less grey than the rest. In the laboratory, this can be made clearer by shining ultraviolet light across the upperwing. As Barn Owls do not begin moult until their second calendar-year, juveniles can be told apart by their more pointed unabraded primaries, which are all silvery-white with uniform sheen; the small hidden (eleventh) primary also appears clean and white. First- and second-year adults can also usually be told apart: Barn Owls a year or more old usually have a new glossy white sixth primary among the slightly duller and greyer ones, and two-year-olds exhibit clean and glossy fourth, fifth, seventh and eighth primaries. Birds which are three years old often show glossy first, second, third, ninth and tenth primaries. However, some birds which are four, five or six years old can show similar character-istics to the two- and three-year-olds so it is usually safe to conclude only that Barn Owls are two years old or more in this situation.

When young birds still in the nest experience temporary prey shortage, perhaps because of the adults' inability to hunt successfully during bad weather, this stress can manifest itself as a fault bar or narrow ring around each of the developing feather shafts which will remain until the feathers are moulted. Although it is not common to find these on the flight feathers, they sometimes appear across the tail quills. Because replacement of the tail takes place over a two-year period, fault bars running in the same position across all tail feathers provide additional evidence that a bird is a juvenile.

The Institute of Terrestrial Ecology uses these methods to age Barn Owls in its mortality studies (Newton 1991). Indeed, the institute has taken ageing further during postmortem examination, by showing that females with straight slender oviducts are pre-breeding-season juveniles and those with thicker, kinked oviducts are adult birds which have previously laid eggs.

Another method of helping to determine the age of Barn Owls in the hand, and one which can be particularly useful for separating juvenile, first-year and second-year birds, is by examining the degree of development of the talon flange, a protuberance of the sheath found on the innermost edge of the middle talon. Observations of preening birds show that this is used to comb the edge of the facial disc and the bristles surrounding the gape. An extensive study by Paul Johnson (1991) found that, of 147 wild young Barn Owls in 42 broods, none possessed a serrated flange when it fledged. Growth studies involving 56 captive Barn Owls showed that development of the flange was insignificant until the owl was nine weeks old, at which age a noticeable smooth ridge formed along the length of the inner edge of the third talon. Between twelve weeks and seven months, the ridge remained smooth but widened to between 1.5 mm on males and 2.0 mm on females. After seven months the smooth flange began to show a distinct notching, and after two years, it became deeply serrated, usually to the base of the flange itself, after which development appeared to cease.

2

HISTORY

Discoveries in France suggest that the genus *Tyto* first appeared some 20 million years ago, about 15 million years after the eagle and eared owls, *Bubo* and *Asio*. These remains, discovered along with other fossil birds, indicate that the country had a fauna akin to Central Africa today. Remains of a barn owl *Tyto giganteo*, which was larger than our present European Eagle Owl, were also found in Italy dating from this period.

Barn Owl bones from 1.75 million years ago discovered in North America, Brazil, the Galapagos, Ireland, New Zealand and Southern Europe, indicate this species's early cosmopolitan nature. Fragments of *T. ostologa* bones from a cave in the Caribbean show that it was about twice the size of *T. alba*, and remains of a barn owl one and a half times its size, dating back about 2 million years, have been found in caves in Mallorca and Menorca. Remains of Barn Owls of three sizes in southern Europe at this period suggest a variety of vertebrate prey including large mammals. Fossils from this time of 44 owl species from all over the world include 39 species of Strigidae, of which ten are extinct and six species of Tytonidae of which five are extinct.

The Barn Owl is predominantly a bird of open country and its long wings and low wing loading would have been generally unsuited to the widespread forest environment which covered almost two-thirds of Britain's land surface and which dominated the post-glacial period 10,000 years ago. Evidence for the Barn Owl's probable recolonization of suitable areas, has been found at Cresswell Crags on the Nottinghamshire-Derbyshire border where the remains of at least three individuals have been recovered from the upper levels of Pin Hole Cave. These stratigraphic levels contain later artefacts from about 10,000 years ago. A rich variety of suitable prey species were also found, including Common, Short-tailed, Gregarious and Root Voles, together with large numbers of Arctic Lemmings. A particular feature of these levels is large numbers of remains of frogs and toads, amounting to over 300 individuals. Of particular interest were a number of owl pellets consisting entirely of amphibian remains (Jenkinson 1984).

At this time, the Barn Owl would probably have been confined to the unafforested habitats around the coast, estuaries, marshy areas and fenland fringes of the river valleys, perhaps accounting for its apparent preference for small amphibians. Here it probably nested in the rocky crevices of cliffs and within the hollows of isolated trees where these were available. Nevertheless the Tawny Owl probably dominated because of the widespread deciduous forests which flourished in the warm moist climate. With the arrival of Neolithic man about 4500 years ago, woodland clearance began in earnest.

Bronze and Iron Age Men achieved massive forest clearance leading to a patchwork of open land and forest. The climate changed and summers became moist and cool. The open grassland and increased woodland-edge habitats would have led to greater availability of small mammals and an expansion of the Barn Owl's range, perhaps at the expense of the Tawny Owl.

Remains of the nominate race of Barn Owl have been found at several prehistoric sites, including the 2500-year-old lake village at Glastonbury, the Roman site of Woodcutt in Dorset and another lake village in County Meath, Ireland. It has also been discovered in many other countries where it is still found, as well as in New Zealand, from where it is now absent.

By Roman times forest cover had halved with human settlements scattered within blocks of ancient forests and agricultural land offering even greater opportunities for the Barn Owl. The creation of more open habitats continued as the number of grazing animals increased and the amount of woodland cover in Britain continued to decline. By the Middle Ages when woodlands were at their lowest point in history, it is likely that Barn Owls were being drawn more and more into urban areas, attracted by rodent infestations of the type responsible for the Black Death in 1345.

As human populations rose in the sixteenth century, concern began to be expressed about the loss of foodstuffs to vermin: in 1532 and 1566 Acts of Parliament were introduced first for controlling grain-eating birds and later other birds and mammals which might impinge on the production and preservation of food. Rabbits were becoming an important source of meat and many birds of prey were included in the later Act. Owls were not mentioned in these Acts and may not have been subject to persecution even though they were probably more closely associated with man than many other birds of prey at this time.

From 1760, drainage and land enclosures, previously largely confined to wool-producing areas of East Anglia, south-west England and Wales, increased quickly throughout Britain. Open fields of inter-mixed strips were parcelled into compact farms, and between 1720 and 1845 over 6,000,000 acres had been dealt with in this way (Fussell 1966). Field sizes decreased from an average 32 ha in 1680 to 6.5 ha by 1839 which was considered manageable using horses. (Pollard 1974). Hedgerows were planted, and the development of boundary hedges, drainage ditches, the continued opening of woodlands and the creation of water meadows greatly increased the amount of grassland edge available for small mammals such as voles, mice and shrews. Even small cornfields had a wide grassy 'walkway' alongside the boundary hedges providing more small-mammal habitat and greater opportunities for Barn Owls to hunt. Potential foraging habitat is likely to have been at its greatest sometime in the late eighteenth and early nineteenth centuries: in the mid to late eighteenth century naturalists and writers described the Barn Owl as both widely distributed and numerous.

The increase in corn production for the growing human and livestock populations meant a greater need for the bulk storage of grain and led to corn ricks becoming commonplace in the stackyards of most farms. More horses were required to handle the increased workload and this led to more

Barn owls prospered in rickyards and straw-bedded stables where small rodents swarmed providing a dependable food source even in the most severe winters.

Hilary Burn

straw-bedded stables on farms: together with stacks of unthreshed wheat, oats, barley, beans and hay and straw ricks these provided warm and sheltered prey-rich habitats for small mammals allowing them to breed throughout the year. Commonly, stackyards consisted of between two and six individual ricks of wheat, oats or barley or occasionally beans, built in August and threshed at any time from September through to the July.

Ricks were fenced at the time of threshing and the numbers of rats and mice recorded. A study in the early 1940s by the Agricultural Research Council found that the corn rick was a habitat of major importance for rats and mice, constituting their main winter breeding areas. The study, devised to assess the rodent numbers contained within these ricks, concluded that maximum densities were attained in February through to May, as a result of continuous breeding in this warm and food-rich micro-habitat. It was shown, for example, that a stackyard of six ricks could, by March, attract a population of 1200. Of the 605 rats present in this particular study, over 30 per cent were below 44 g body weight and 50 per cent below 95 g (Venables and Leslie 1942). Since Barn Owls have been found to take rats ranging in size from 25–164 g (Morris 1979), this provided a potential prey population probably in excess of 1000 small commensal rodents, largely confined within the limits of one yard, their zone of activity determined by the accessibility of nearby water, commonly the farm pond. The Bank Vole, Wood Mouse, and Harvest Mouse were also attracted to these ricks and like rats, were able to reproduce through the winter (Frank 1957).

Other indications of the rodent density of rickyards can be obtained from the number of Brown Rats killed and recorded by gamekeepers (Twigg 1975). For example, in 1903 a single keeper on an estate in East Anglia killed 14,662 rats. In 1926, over 10,000 were killed, but by 1942 following the advent of the combine harvester and the loss of ricks, numbers decreased to 1500 although keepering pressures remained constant. The last estimate in 1966 was 466: today, farmers have at their disposal an armoury of chemical rodenticides which can maintain rodents at very low levels.

Commensal rodents were more important to the Barn Owl's diet early in the century: a study by Collinge in *Economic Ornithology* written between 1924 and 1927, showed that the Brown Rat and House Mouse constituted about 58 per cent of the diet by weight. In 1935 Ticehurst, too, found that these rodents comprised 43 per cent of the bird's nutritional requirements.

In the Agricultural Research Council's study, Barn Owls were shown to be a major predator at infested ricks, not only hunting the barn floor and surrounding areas, but also nesting in the tunnel which ran at the level of the eaves for cooling purposes. Although no comprehensive study was made of pellet remains during this study, at one site they were analysed: rats constituted approximately 80 per cent of the prey species. The rickyard thus provided a rich dependable source of food at a time during the winter when small mammals of open grassland would have been in short supply.

The carrying capacity of the environment is likely to have been highest for the Barn Owl in the first half of the nineteenth century: only 10 per cent of Britain's land surface remained as woodland and prey-rich stackyards were common. My study of old county bird books showed that Barn Owl numbers began to fall by about 1825, after the advent of organized pheasant rearing. By 1850, gamekeepers were employed to destroy predators which they were able to do more efficiently following the invention of the breech-loading gun and pole trap. Taxidermy and egg collecting also flourished and Barn Owls were prized as mantlepiece 'ornaments', their wings used for firescreens and feathers for millinery.

Unlike Sparrowhawks, which remained common over much of Britain throughout the worst persecution because they could remain inconspicuous (Newton 1986), Barn Owls were more vulnerable. Keepers knew the traditional breeding places and others would have been found by locals to sell the bodies to the lucrative London markets. The Barn Owl could be found and killed at its nest comparatively easily, and the long period over which the young remain in the nest enabled keepers to destroy whole broods.

During this time of intense persecution a succession of hard winters from 1860–1900 caused a further blow for the Barn Owl and these problems were further compounded by changing patterns of farming as the Agricultural Revolution began Underground field drainage was invented and the practical application of steam power for threshing and ploughing began. Ditches, hedgerows and hedgerow trees and their associated grasslands were removed and small enclosed fields enlarged to suit the new equipment and rapidly increasing demands for food.

The first evidence of any improvement in attitudes towards the Barn Owl appeared in county reports in about 1880, heralding greater awareness of the bird. Statements in late nineteenth-century literature emphasized the importance of the Barn Owl in controlling rodent pests. These, coupled with the introduction of bird protection laws beginning in Northumberland in 1869 and 1872 and leading to the Wild Birds' Protection Act of 1880 and legislation outlawing the use of the poletrap in 1904, were responsible for increasing public awareness and for reducing the slaughter of birds.

The first reports of recovery appeared early in the twentieth century, particularly in northern England and southern Scotland. The number of gamekeepers fell during World War I, recovering only slightly before World War II, after which it fell again to around 5000. The prolonged succession of snow-free winters up until 1940, coupled with the relaxation of persecution pressure, was probably responsible for the noticeable increase in numbers.

Towards the end of the nineteenth century most counties in England and a number in Wales published avifauna, providing some indication of the bird's standing. By combining information from works published between 1871 and 1929, I obtained a picture of the Barn Owl's regional distribution and abundance in Britain and Ireland around the turn of the century. It was still common across south-east England, except in Norfolk and Lincolnshire. It was considered uncommon or scarce in much of south-western and northern England and south-western and northern Scotland and only fairly common in the midlands. Where the Barn Owl had declined, persecution was almost always cited as the sole cause. In south-eastern England, however, when the bird was still noted as common, authors rarely alluded to persecution and its regional fortunes may have been dictated by local superstition.

3

DISTRIBUTION

In the UK, the white-breasted Barn Owl, first described by Scopoli from specimens in Italy in 1769, is the typical or nominate race *alba*. Predominantly a Mediterranean form, it is found, if uncommonly, in parts of Turkey and Bulgaria, western Greece, Albania, Croatia and Slovenia, Italy and southern Switzerland. Its range extends west through Sicily and the Balearics to Tenerife and Gran Canaria, north to Portugal, Spain, southern and western France to the Channel Islands, Belgium and Britain and Ireland. The dark-breasted *guttata* (Brehm 1831) is better suited to the colder regions of Europe and is dominant north and east of the 3 °C January isotherm, in central and eastern France, Germany, Luxembourg, The Netherlands, Denmark, the Czech Republic, Austria, Poland, Slovakia, Hungary, Switzerland, Romania, Belorussia, western Ukraine, Lithuania and Latvia. The two races overlap at the 3 °C January isotherm and interbreed in eastern Belgium, northern and eastern France, the western limits of Germany and probably in northern Italy, parts of Croatia and Slovenia, Albania, Greece, Bulgaria and Turkey.

Four island races are also found in Europe: *ernisti*, confined to Corsica and Sardinia, *erlangeri* in Crete and Cyprus (as well as North Africa and the Middle East), *schmitzi* in Madeira, Porto Santo and the Desertas, and *gracilirostris* in Fuerteventura, Lanzarote and Aleqranza in the eastern Canaries.

Population in Europe

Current data from BirdLife International has shown that the Barn Owl breeds across Europe except in Fennoscandia and Malta and is absent from Greenland. The European population (the two main races *alba* and *guttata*) is estimated at 110–230,000 breeding pairs, with three-quarters of these in Spain, Portugal, France and Italy. Although the Barn Owl extends as far north as Denmark and Scotland, it has become uncommon in Europe where the mean January isotherm is 3 °C or below and scarce where January temperatures average 0 °C or below. Its dependence on mild winters is illustrated by the fact that, although the countries which lie at and below the 3 °C isotherm account for two-thirds of the landmass of Europe, they contain about 10 per cent of the Barn Owl population there. Winter temperature, and more specifically snow cover, are undoubtedly the main factors determining the Barn Owl's distribution and abundance in Europe. Although first-year birds occasionally disperse long distances in some parts of continental Europe, Barn Owls are usually resident throughout their European range. In winter the population increases about threefold, but this is based on the assumption that pairs produce on average from two to three young, which leads to a temporary increase in wintering numbers, rather than any influx of birds from elsewhere.

Declining numbers in Europe

Although the Barn Owl is not considered imminently threatened across Europe, it has shown a rapid and long-term decline of 20–50 per cent over the last twenty years in half of the 36 European countries listed. In the mid 1980s it became extinct in Malta, because of persecution, as well as in Fennoscandia, where, at the limit of its northern breeding range, numbers were never high. Major population declines have occurred in central and eastern Europe and in those countries where the mean January isotherm is below 4 °C, indicating low winter temperatures and persistent snow cover.

Fig. 3 *The status of the Barn Owl in Europe. The 3 °C January isotherm marks the west/east division between the nominate T.a. alba (100,000–200,000 pairs) and T.a. guttata (10,000–30,000 pairs), although they interbreed at this division.*

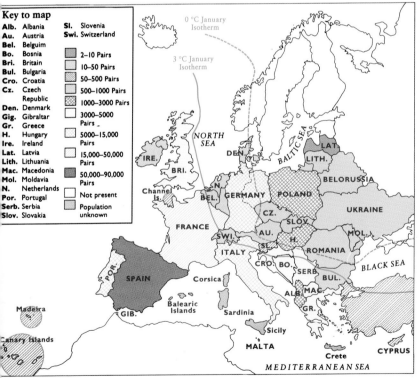

ource: Map compiled from BirdLife International/European Bird Census Council, European Bird Database – September 1993
nd C. Shawyer unpublished.

Czechoslovakia has seen a decline of over 50 per cent in the last twenty years, and like the CIS and much of eastern Europe experiences prolonged snow cover and average winter temperature of 0 °C or below. These countries probably maintain Barn Owls only because their more traditional methods of farming continue to provide prey-rich habitats in winter. Unlike many countries in central and eastern Europe, Poland and Hungary are low-lying, with most of their land below 180 m. As such, they experience somewhat milder winters and as a result, they still collectively appear able to support a population of 2500–6000 pairs, even though numbers have declined in both countries by 20–50 per cent over the last twenty years.

UK population – historical changes

The main aim of the survey I started in 1982 was to obtain a much better understanding of the Barn Owl's distribution and abundance in Britain and Ireland and to attempt to assess the extent of and main reasons for any changes in numbers so that conservation could be undertaken. Obtaining reliable information about this highly elusive species would prove hard enough, but was there enough historical information which could be used to evaluate trends and the factors which were likely to be governing them?

Much of the historical information about the Barn Owl in Britain has been summarized already and, as in the case with most retrospective investigations, was the result of exhaustive literature searches. All of this, however, was clearly going to be needed if I was eventually to be able to put the Barn Owl's present distribution and status into any form of historical perspective and to begin to under and the major factors most likely to be governing any long-term trend the population of this bird.

The 1932 census The first serious attempt to census the Barn Owl in England and Wales was undertaken in 1932 (Blaker 1934). This year also saw the beginnings of a national ringing and recording scheme which differentiated between the numbers of adults and nestlings ringed, allowing meaningful interpretations to be made about the dispersal and survival of Barn Owls and other British birds. George Blaker first appeared in the ornithological literature in *Bird Notes and News* in 1932 for an essay, 'The Barn Owl and the Buzzard'. For this he was awarded the RSPB's Silver Medal in the Public Schools' Essay Competition, but it was at Trinity College, Cambridge, in May 1932 that his pioneering census of the Barn Owl in England and Wales began. This census, which finished in December 1932, enlisted the help of societies, clubs, individual naturalists and the general public, using a carefully designed questionnaire, accompanying map and identification guide. It sought details of the precise location and description of the nesting site and information on clutch size, brood size and fledging success, together with the dates the sites were visited. The survey sheet also asked for information about the availability of potential nesting places, the extent of movement of Barn Owls in and out of the study area in question, and whether the birds were thought to have decreased and, if so, an opinion as to the cause. This census was therefore very much ahead of its time in terms of bird-surveying in Britain.

As a result of these enquiries about 1000 detailed nest-site locations were reported from between 50 and 100 fieldwork organizers, from which 214 individual records of breeding successes were obtained. These data were supplemented by more generalized information from about 4000 other observers, resulting in the notification of more than 5000 breeding locations. These provided a basis for estimating the species' abundance in England and Wales, at 12,000 pairs and 1000 additional individuals. The census results appeared in *Bird Notes and News* in 1933, and produced as a pamphlet by the RSPB in 1934 in which Barn Owl abundance was mapped for every 10-mile (16-km) square in England and Wales (*see* Fig. 4 overleaf).

Blaker himself drew attention to the possible limitations of his survey, stating that most of the conclusions arrived at were based on collective opinion, but his pioneering census provided the baseline for assessing future changes in the Barn Owl population. One factor not known then but which we now recognize from more than fifty years of years of bird-ringing, is that Barn Owl populations oscillate from one year to the next in line with the cyclical changes in small-mammal numbers and climatic factors, so that a single-year survey does not necessarily tell us whether or not the 12,000 pairs estimated related to a year when numbers were at a peak or a trough, or somewhere between. An analysis of the ringing records for the period suggests that Barn Owl numbers may have been at their height in 1933, and, from the little evidence we have, vole numbers seem to have peaked in some parts of Britain in 1932 and 1933 (Snow 1968), which would indicate that Blaker's census may have been conducted at a time when Barn Owl numbers were reaching a temporary peak in the cycle.

Blaker concluded that the Barn Owl's decline had been gradual since 1900, becoming most noticeable in the counties of central and southern England in 1922 and 1928. With hindsight and the knowledge that climatic extremes can play an important part in affecting Barn Owl breeding success and overall numbers, we find that two of the most severe climatic events actually occurred in 1921 and 1927, the years immediately prior to the population declines noted by Blaker. In 1921, Britain suffered the worst summer drought since 1868, which, as we have seen, can seriously reduce small-mammal numbers. In addition, 1927 registered the wettest summer since 1879 (and it remains so to this day), which is likely to have affected the bird's ability to hunt and therefore to have influenced its breeding success. As if this were not enough, the winters of 1928 and 1929 were two of the five most severe during the forty years from 1900 to 1939. The onset of the two periods of accelerating decline in 1922 and 1928 which were reported on the recording sheets of the fieldworkers, and noted in Blaker's report, were probably indicative of the temporary crashes in Barn Owl numbers with which we are now more familiar and from which the population generally bounces back.

In Devon, parts of Somerset and Cornwall, the Barn Owl was said to be holding its own, while in the northern counties of England Blaker reported that Barn Owls were showing a noticeable increase in numbers which was probably due to the increase in rank grassland following afforestation there, by the newly formed Forestry Commission in 1919, coupled with a general

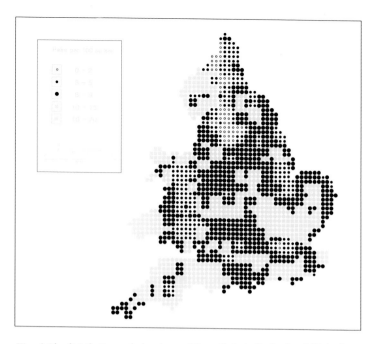

Fig. 4 *The distribution and abundance of Barn Owls in England and Wales in 1932* (source: Blaker)

amelioration of the climate which began in 1900. In overall terms, therefore, the Barn Owl population had probably remained relatively stable in England and Wales in the two to three decades leading up to the census. Whatever was happening in terms of population change, however, Blaker's work provided an extremely important record of the Barn Owl population in England and Wales in 1932, and his work, a credit to ornithology, was justly awarded the RSPB's Gold Medal in 1934.

Changing numbers during the 1950s and 1960s The only other attempt to assess the extent of changing numbers of Barn Owls (and other smaller birds of prey and corvids) was conducted by Prestt in 1965. This study sought largely subjective opinions from BTO regional representatives and a wide cross-section of the general public about the degree of population change between the years 1953 and 1963. Opinions were analysed from 141 completed questionnaires. The findings were far from clear-cut and, although it was concluded that the Barn Owl had undergone a decline, in no region was this considered very marked. Some thought the decline temporary in nature, while others believed that it was part of a longer-term trend over this period. A moderate decrease had, however, been found in all the counties of the eastern half of England (with the possible exception of Norfolk), as well as in Lancashire, Cheshire, Somerset, Dorset, Devon and Cornwall and parts of Gloucestershire, and a higher level of decline in South Wales and the Isle of Man.

Declines were shown to be most apparent in 1958. Once again, this can be traced to a year of climatic extreme when, during that exceptionally wet

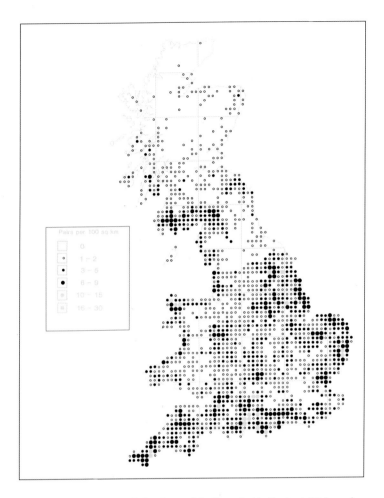

Fig. 5 *The distribution and abundance of the Barn Owl in England, Wales and Scotland at the end of the last survey in 1985.*

summer, no young Barn Owls were ringed in Britain, the only time this has happened (and it was also the worst year on record for Tawny Owls according to the classic work by Southern). After 1958, the very severe winters of 1962 and 1963 occurred, the latter noted for its unprecedented severity this century when an average of 63 days of snow cover was recorded at a selection of low-lying meteorological stations in the British Isles. It was significant that worsening climate was actually a factor given by the respondents to this survey as one reason for the Barn Owl's changing status.

Once again, as well as suggesting that organochlorine pesticides were probably to blame, the results could also be attributed to the probable decline in winter prey caused by the increases in winter severity and the disappearance of the stackyard in the cereal-dominated regions. Indeed, the reasons given by the survey workers for the changes which were seen were by no means unanimous, with pesticides actually coming second to the combined loss of habitat and food supply in the scoring system used by Prestt to determine the importance of the many contributory causes. In 1986, the Atlas of Breeding Birds in Britain and Ireland found 2279 10-km squares occupied and the population was estimated at between 4500 and 9000 breeding pairs over the period 1968–72 (Sharrock 1976).

The present This now brings us up to the present time and the survey of Britain and Ireland that I conducted between 1982 and 1985. Because of the increased knowledge of the temporary changes which can occur in Barn Owl populations, it was decided to conduct this survey over a three-year period. In the event, data from the pilot year in 1982 were added, so it effectively covered four calendar-years, spanning one complete vole cycle.

Some 11,500 records were eventually obtained, of which 15 per cent were rejected instantly, either because there was some doubt about their validity or because the map reference given could not allow the record to be placed accurately within a 1-km square. At this stage my colleague, the late Peter Banks, began writing the necessary computer programmes and preparing the data in a form suitable for entry onto computer. This allowed instant scrutiny of 35,000 squares which could be panned from square to square and county to county in any direction across the screen.

Each individual record which had survived previous checks was scrutinized again and rechecked against the appropriate Ordnance Survey maps. Particular care was taken with regard to the map reference and category of observation and whether it was a breeding record or a breeding-season or winter sighting. In addition to the information supplied about the type of nest site, main habitat and farming types, observers' experience etc., data were also included with each record on the height above sea level, proximity to a waterway or wetland, motorway or railway and the average annual rainfall. In all, facilities were available for the entry of up to thirty discrete pieces of information for each individual record. These could be sorted, ordered, searched, selected and printed on the basis of Vice-Counties or 10-km squares.

The five different ranges of abundance for each 10-km square were used to compile the final map and to allow direct comparison with Blaker's work, which had been converted from 10-mile squares to 10-km squares. Ranges of abundance were chosen because it was clearly not possible, except in the most thoroughly searched squares, to guarantee that all the sites had been found. Fig. 5 on page 31 represents the total number of breeding sites estimated for each 10-km square from a total of 2699 confirmed and 2301 probable breeding records during the full survey period from 1982 to 1985.

The map shows that the Barn Owl was almost as widely distributed in England and Wales in 1982–85 as it was in 1932. The new survey, however, included Scotland and Ireland, and in the former country it was, not surprisingly, restricted mainly to the southern lowlands and the Western Isles, where winters are mild. The general distribution was similar to that in 1968–72 shown in the *Atlas of Breeding Birds in Britain and Ireland*: this owl remained widely distributed, being found in 50 per cent of all 10-km squares in Britain and Ireland, but was absent from rural areas and most regions of high ground over 150 m above sea-level, which held only 7 per cent of the breeding population.

The 1980s survey established a population in England and Wales of about 3750 pairs with an additional 650 pairs in Scotland; in the Channel Isles, the current population fell within the range 32 to 46 pairs. In Ireland, the lack of observers prevented adequate coverage and only the presence or absence of breeding pairs was recorded, but taking the average of about two to three pairs per 10-km square (based upon information from well-covered squares), gave a total of between 600 to 900 pairs. In Britain and Ireland as a whole the breeding population was therefore estimated at 5000 pairs (Shawyer 1987).

The extent of the decline Blaker estimated 12,000 breeding pairs of Barn Owls in England and Wales in 1932, which on the basis of the present data indicates a 69 per cent decrease in numbers during the last fifty years. While numbers in Scotland and Ireland have undoubtedly shown a significant decline also, the lack of any past numerical data makes the extent of this impossible to determine. The population figures for the period 1982–85 are shown alongside those estimated in 1932 for each of the counties of England and Wales (Figs 6 and 7 overleaf). These figures enabled the extent of population change in each county to be determined and compared with the overall decline in England and Wales of 69 per cent. The extent to which the population was threatened was also assessed on the basis of its density within each vice-county. Populations averaging between 0–2.5 pairs per 10-km square were considered critical, i.e., likely to decline further or become extinct over the next fifty years. Those between 2.6 and 4.0 pairs were described as vulnerable, and likely to move into the critical category soon if no conservation action was taken. Populations above 4.0 pairs per 10-km square were considered stable: in other words, viable in the foreseeable future if conditions remained the same. It was found that populations were critical in 63 per cent of the vice-counties, vulnerable in 17 per cent and stable in 20 per cent.

Level of protection The general scarcity of the Barn Owl in the 1960s coupled with its apparent long-term decline, resulted in the species being added in 1966 to the list of rarities in Part 1 of the First Schedule of the Protection of Birds Act 1954, now listed under Schedule 1 of the Wildlife and Countryside Act 1981, which provides it with special protection over and above that given to many other wild birds. It is also listed on the European Community Birds Directive, which charges all member states to protect all wild birds and preserve sufficient diversity of habitat to maintain populations at an ecologically and scientifically sound level, and Appendix II of the Berne Convention carries an obligation to protect flora and fauna and their habitats, especially those listed as endangered or vulnerable.

Although my own recent survey of Britain and Ireland showed a population in Britain and Ireland of about 5000 pairs (and a decline of 69 per cent over fifty years), these data were considered insufficient to determiner to population had halved over the last 20 years which was one of the main criteria for inclusion in the *Red Data Book* (Batten 1990) as an

Fig. 6 *County Population estimates and extent of decline 1932–1982/85*

	1932	1882/5	% change		1932	1882/5	% change
England				W. Midlands	65	20	–69
Cornwall	340	270	–21	Warwickshire	200	50	–75
Devon	710	235	–67	Staffordshire	180	35	–81
Somerset	355	150	–58	Lincolnshire	510	200	–61
Avon	30	5	–85	Leicestershire & Rutland	245	25	–90
Wiltshire	255	115	–55	Nottinghamshire	210	95	–55
Dorset	275	110	–60	Derbyshire	245	40	–84
Isle of Wight	29	51	+76	Cheshire	240	35	–85
Hampshire	350	145	–59	Lancashire, incl. Mersey-			
W. Sussex	186	75	–60	side & Gtr Manchester	265	85	–68
E. Sussex	216	63	–71	Humberside	190	125	–34
Kent	320	90	–72	N. Yorkshire	410	55	–89
Surrey	137	34	–75	S. and W. Yorkshire	200	50	–75
Essex	470	120	–74	Co. Durham, Tyne &			
Hertfordshire	210	10	–95	Wear & Cleveland	155	35	–77
Middlesex	30	2	–93	Northumberland	150	50	–67
Berkshire	120	40	–67	Cumbria	745	120	–84
Oxfordshire	130	45	–65	Isle of Man	5	5	
Buckinghamshire	160	20	–88				
Suffolk	345	150	–57	**Wales**			
Norfolk	445	190	–57	Glamorgan	105	35	–67
Cambridgeshire	215	45	–57	Gwent	120	25	–79
Bedfordshire	140	30	–79	Powys	210	50	–76
Northamptonshire	250	50	–80	Dyfed	535	165	–69
Gloucestershire	225	70	–69	Gwynedd	275	145	–47
Herefordshire	190	50	–74	Clwyyd	170	40	–76
Worcestershire	185	30	–84				

Fig. 7 *Population estimates in Scotland during 1982/85 survey*

Dumfries and Galloway	275	Tayside	25
Strathclyde and Inner Hebrides	195	Grampian	45
Borders	80	Highland	25
Lothian	25	Western Isles	0
Fife	15	Orkney	0
Central	15	Shetland	0

endangered, vulnerable or rare species. Thankfully, an additional category, 'Species of Special Concern', was instigated to include the Barn Owl, Black Grouse, Merlin, Greenshank, Whimbrel and Nightjar.

Figures from the new as yet unpublished BTO *Atlas* suggest that the decline is continuing apace, with the number of 10-km squares occupied by Barn Owls in Britain and Ireland dropping from 2279 (59 per cent) in 1972, to 1931 (49 per cent) in 1985 and 1481 (38 per cent) in 1992 (Gibbons in press). Even though the surveys are not strictly comparable because of their different methodologies, the apparent acceleration of decline justifies the Barn Owl's inclusion in the *Red Data Book*. Indeed, the new bird atlas for my own county of Hertfordshire will show a decrease in breeding records, from proven in 33 tetrads and probable in 26 between 1968 and 1972 (Mead 1982), to just seven proven and thirteen probable sites twenty years later (Shawyer and Dockerty in Smith in press).

4

HABITAT

In Britain, Barn Owls can be found in a wide variety of habitat types but are almost always associated with open grassland and woodland edge. It is still widely believed that this owl is dependent solely on mixed traditional farmland which comprises small fields of cattle and crops interspersed with water meadows and marshy land. While it is true that these habitats remain important and need protection, Barn Owl densities in the UK are actually greater in, for example, the fenlands of east Lincolnshire and the heavily afforested areas of southern Scotland, regions notorious for intensive land management where monocultures of cereals and conifers prevail. The value of these habitats lies in their extensive and largely unmanaged rough-grassland margins, and it is these which are responsible for relatively high and stable populations in these regions.

The banks of field-drainage ditches in Lincolnshire, and the interface between maturing forest and moorland and grassy strips along woodland rides and forest tracks in Scotland provide a concentrated food source over a set beat, familiarity with which can result in high capture rates. These

The rough grassy margins of fields and ditches are the perfect hunting areas for Barn Owls on farmland today.

regions of intensively cropped land each covering some 1500 km^2 provide linear continuity of rough grassland, offering opportunities for the safe and successful dispersal of young birds and the integrity of a viable population.

Size

My own studies in Lincolnshire have shown that, in the breeding season, Barn Owls usually concentrate most of their hunting within 1–2 km of the nest but will range up to 4 km or more, although foraging takes place only over a proportion of the home range. Within the average hunting area of 3 km^2 (300 ha), each of the ten pairs studied had at its disposal 15–25 km of rough grassland margin averaging 6 m wide, equivalent to about 8–10 ha. Breeding pairs were rarely found, however, where the length of grassland edge fell below this, in spite of adequate and in some cases a surplus of suitable nesting and roosting opportunities (Shawyer 1988). Similar studies conducted in south Scotland have indicated that the extent of woodland edge within the 3-km^2 hunting range dictated whether or not breeding Barn Owls were present and the breeding success of those which were. It has been shown that 4–5 km of woodland edge are required within a 1-km radius of the nest before breeding occurs and that 9–11 km of grassy edge are needed for Barn Owls to produce an average of 3.0 to 3.5 fledged young, which was considered the level of productivity necessary for maintaining a self-sustaining population in this region (Taylor 1989).

In most other regions of Britain where farming is predominantly of single enterprise and the land has been maximized for crops or livestock, Barn Owls are rarely found, because open ditches and hedgerows have been removed along with their associated grassy margins.

Elsewhere, Barn Owls favour sites where there are sufficiently large areas of rank grassland, such as old parkland in Norfolk, damp pastures in Anglesey, flood meadows in Somerset and coastal marshes in Suffolk, as well as the often vast grasslands of military lands. In these more traditional habitats, they seem to require about 50 ha (120 acres) of suitable grassland within their normal hunting range of 3 km^2 (Brazil 1989). Nevertheless, Barn Owls rarely maintain viability if these grasslands are in isolated pockets, since they need to be part of a landscape where such habitats are widespread and Barn Owls are most commonly found breeding within 1 km or so of a main river or stream, and in many regions of Britain the majority of sites are linked by these riparian corridors.

Altitude and snow duration

In general, Barn Owls breed at low altitude in the UK, although a small proportion is found in upland regions of grass moorland, forest and sheepwalk. This is largely because of the restricted range of prey species and the greater depth and duration of snow cover found at these higher altitudes. Small mammals become hidden beneath the snow blanket in winter, reducing feeding opportunities, for the owls which in turn affects their breeding success and in more extreme situations, increases mortality.

The 1982–5 Barn Owl Survey showed that, of the 2699 breeding sites logged, 2510 (93 per cent) were found below 150 m where annual snow cover averaged fifteen days or less. 150 m appears to be close to the upper limit for this species in the UK, and birds breeding above this height were found mainly in counties bordering the western seaboard, where snow cover is substantially less because of the milder maritime influences.

Composition of grassland

The main habitat requirements for the Barn Owl's favoured prey, the Short-tailed Vole, Wood Mouse and Common Shrew, is rank or rough grassland with a thick sward and deep litter layer. Young soft grasses provide food, fallen grass stems offer shelter, and tussocks nesting places, and invertebrate food for the shrew. A thick surface mat of such grasses as False Oat-grass, Slender False Brome, Meadow Fescue and Cock's-foot, together with other species which are soft and nutritious, such as Meadow Soft, Brown Bent, Fiorin Grass and Meadow Fox-tail allows voles and shrews both to feed and to construct concealed runways and feeding chambers between their nests. In grazed or cropped grasslands this thatch or litter layer cannot build up.

Optimal habitat for these two small mammals, and thus for Barn Owls, seems to be largely unmanaged grasslands. In the prey-rich situations around Scottish conifer forests and the drainage ditches of the fens, most of the 'management' is natural: wind and rainfall consolidate the litter layer, and the activities of small mammals, light grazing by small numbers of cattle and, in some places, browsing by deer prevent scrub forming.

While perennial grass swards largely manage themselves, scrub will eventually develop and some form of periodic management such as mowing or grazing becomes necessary, every third year or so. More frequent grazing and the non-rotational close-mowing common on river banks today destroy the tussock structure and should be avoided. A three-year research project by The Hawk and Owl Trust is investigating more thoroughly the ecology of the Short-tailed Vole to develop a more detailed habitat prescription to assist in the conservation of threatened birds of prey, such as the Barn Owl.

Nest-site selection

The Barn Owl normally needs a large chamber in which to nest, and in the British Isles it is usually one of three main types: inside buildings, large tree cavities and rock fissures. Thomas Pennant in 1776 indicated it was equally at home in trees and buildings, and a century later Alfred Yarrell listed hollow trees second to church towers and farm buildings as the most usual site. George Blaker in 1934 quantified the relative importance of these in England and Wales, showing that 44 per cent were in hollow trees, 53 per cent in buildings and 2.8 per cent in cliff-like situations.

It would seem logical to expect the Barn Owl to be opportunist in its choice of nesting site, selecting those sites most abundant in its particular area, but an analysis of the 2700 nest site descriptions reported in the

Nest sites in buildings are much more common in western Britain.

1982–85 survey suggested that the choice of site was dictated by climate. Rainfall varies considerably in different regions of the British Isles, being much heavier in the south and west (influenced by prevailing moist south-westerly winds from the Atlantic), where annual rainfall averages between 100 and 320 cm while in much of eastern Britain it rarely exceeds 65 cm.

The Barn Owl's soft, little-oiled plumage rapidly becomes saturated, making hunting difficult. In spring and summer heavy rainfall can affect breeding success by reducing the amount of food provided by the male and wet nest sites can cause the death of young fledglings through chilling and disease. Even after the critical period of nesting, heavy rainfall can prove hazardous to newly emerging and inexperienced young, which spend considerable time in long rank grass while learning to hunt. They easily become waterlogged, and unable to return to the security of the breeding site, die. Thus in districts where rainfall is consistently prolonged, the selection of dry sites is of prime importance. The survey established that, although the percentage of building (66 per cent) to tree (33 per cent) nest sites in England and Wales was similar to that found by Blaker, in those regions where opposing extremes of rainfall occur there are marked variations. In the south and west, where rainfall is highest, 95 per cent of the breeding population nest in buildings. In the east, however, where rainfall is light and winds drying, hollow tree sites predominate: in Suffolk over 70 per cent of Barn Owls nest in trees, more than twice the national average.

Only a small proportion of the county bird books of the late 1800s gave details about the major class of nest site used. A number of authors, however, indicated that trees were the predominant site in the east. Buildings were reported to be the Barn Owl's exclusive choice in the western counties, Sussex and much of Ireland and Scotland. Despite habitat changes, there is no evidence of regional differences in nest-site selection over the last century, which lends support to the idea that rainfall, a stable long-term phenomenon, is important in determining nest sites.

While buildings are most commonly used in Scotland, rock fissures are important around the coast, particularly in western districts such as Argyll and on the Inner Hebrides, where cliffs and caves constitute about 50 per cent of breeding sites as the choice of nest site is restricted, with suitable buildings and trees being rare. Here, rock crevices and cavities in earthen cliffs and banks sometimes provide the only secure site for nesting.

Sites within spacious old cottages and farm buildings, as opposed to smaller tree cavities, discourage early fledging which can have disastrous consequences during prolonged wet weather. Observations confirm that the young, having left the nest, often spend days in the shelter of the building, exercising and practising hunting before venturing forth. In the drier climate of the east, the need for sheltered sites is unlikely to be so critical.

Trees Old isolated trees in pastures, parkland and hedgerows are the most commonly used site and despite the ravages of Dutch Elm Disease old

Holes in rocky outcrops are believed to be the original nesting sites for Barn Owls before barns and other man-made structures were available.

trees still remain a distinctive if declining feature of traditional farmland and old parkland in Britain.

Oak, English Elm and Ash are the most commonly used, because they are the most abundant large trees in the British Isles with sufficient girth to provide the dry and spacious cavities favoured by the Barn Owl. These cavities are mostly located in the main trunk or, in pollards, near the crown. Very few are found in hollow branches (a site favoured by Little and to some extent Tawny Owls) because they rarely provide large enough cavities.

In the mid-1970s the Elm would have provided more potential nest sites than at any other time, and even in 1985 it accounted for one-third of trees used in Britain and Ireland. Dutch Elm Disease, which took a strong hold in southern Britain in the late 1960s, actually benefited the Barn Owl The peak period of nest-site suitability in Elms probably occurred in central-southern England between 1975 and 1978, when most of these trees were in an advanced stage of disease but had not fallen or been felled. This disease has been far less aggressive both in Cornwall, where the English Elm is replaced by the Cornish Elm, and in East Sussex, where 53,000 English Elms remained in 1985 because of sanitation felling. In Suffolk and parts of east Essex, too, only 50–70 per cent of Elms were affected in 1983 compared with 90 per cent elsewhere in southern Britain; perhaps this reflects the counties' isolation from the heavily infected areas inland or the occurrence of a different elm species (Small-leaved Elm) and other hybrids.

Very few Barn owls now nest in church towers in Britain, as these have been wired off against Jackdaws and pigeons.

During courtship flight, the male pursues his mate in and out of potential nest sites.

Ash trees rot out earlier than many others, and with the almost total loss of the Elm since my survey was completed the Ash has now become the preferred hedgerow tree, although in young Ash trees cavities are usually too small. Pollarded willows and beech are the fourth and fifth most commonly used trees, and any tree which provides a large enough cavity makes a potential site if it is relatively isolated and free from disturbance.

Man-made structures In the British Isles, farm buildings represent 70 per cent of all man-made structures used by Barn Owls for nesting, followed by domestic dwellings which are usually derelict (14 per cent), industrial or commercial buildings, including water towers (4.6 per cent), 'castles' (4.3 per cent) and churches (3.2 per cent). Other sites represent less than 1.5 per cent.

Most sites in farm buildings were subject to some form of use, bale stacks, pigeon lofts, holes in walls, and nestboxes providing the necessary seclusion. Domestic buildings were more important in northern England and Scotland where disused cottages were more commonplace often having been vacated by people when land had been sold for afforestation.

In 1932 domestic dwellings and churches combined accounted for 13 per cent of total nest sites. Although churches were once a common site, access became limited as towers were wired off against Jackdaws and pigeons, and they have now become a less important site for Barn Owls.

Nesting on or within loose hay and straw, or more usually bales, is very common, accounting for 39 per cent of agricultural sites, a number of which were in isolated field stacks. Usually these were undisturbed or old ricks which had been in place for a season or more. In 1932, too, this was a common site ricks and hay-filled lofts providing the nesting places. While stacks appear to offer a high degree of security at the beginning of the year, they become progressively vulnerable as bales are removed during the spring, when many eggs and young are inadvertently destroyed.

In domestic buildings, the space on the ceiling boards between the joists of upper floors and attics is most frequently used, and blocked chimneys provide the alternative. Nests on or within stone walls account for many sites, particularly in old castles, common in Ireland. Included here are nests in disused cavities and heating ducts in old Victorian walled gardens.

Nestboxes now provide an important proportion of nesting places, and in 1992 over 800 boxes provided by the Hawk and Owl Trust were occupied in Britain. That these birds readily take to them shows that they are secure and that in some areas natural nest sites are becoming limited even where new habitat is becoming available or is being actively restored.

Only spacious cavities are usually chosen for nesting, the Oak, English Elm and Ash being the most commonly used. Tree sites are preferred in Eastern Britain.

Roosting sites My study of five breeding Barn Owl pairs in south-west Scotland revealed that each regularly used between three and five roosts, to which they showed a high level of fidelity. Most were in farm buildings or derelict cottages next to open sheepwalk. In three pairs, the male and female were regularly found roosting together during the winter: this was not always at the traditional nest site but at the place to which the female had retired after moving away from the young during the previous season. The members of the other two pairs roosted alone until they joined up again in the late winter. Food caching was very common at these winter roosts, particularly during periods of bad weather between December and March.

Once egg-laying began, the male would move away and begin roosting elsewhere. This roost was always close to and in view of the nest, sometimes in the same or an adjacent building, or in a nearby stand of mature conifers. This suggests a definite need to defend the nest and his mate from over-adventurous suitors. Usually the male was faithful to a single roost at this time, but when an alternative was used it was close by. Once the young were four weeks old, brooding usually ceased and the female then moved away herself, selecting a daytime roost often 0.5–1.0 km from the nest. At the same time, three of the male birds selected a new night-time roost up to 1.5 km from the nest or would begin to roost with the female again. The other two males remained at their daytime roost, close to the nest.

5

FOOD AND FEEDING

The quality and type of food an animal eats is the most important factor determining its reproductive performance, its population density and its survival. For the Barn Owl, the amount of prey needs to be high, especially during the period before breeding in February and March and through the nesting period from April to September, when the food demands of a pair of owls increases from about 10–40 prey items a day.

Because Barn Owls usually swallow their prey whole and are incapable of digesting much bone, pellet contents can prove very revealing. It is usually possible to identify from these remains, particularly intact skulls, the species of prey which were taken and, if necessary, their sex and ages.

The Barn Owl is a specialist feeder on small mammals, in particular voles, mice, shrews and young rats. Today, it is the Short-tailed Vole or Field Vole that is the most nutritionally important prey item in mainland Britain (Glue 1974). The vole is followed closely by the Wood Mouse, which, although also a grassland species, tends to be confined to lowland areas, being prevalent in open agricultural landscapes around rough grassy

Rank, tussocky grassland provides the ideal habitat for Barn Owls to hunt over and find their main prey – the Field Vole.

field margins, deciduous woodlands and woodland edges, where it feeds on seeds, fruit and invertebrates (Flowerdew 1984). I have, however, found that the Wood Mouse, which is lighter than the vole, can assume primary importance in weight terms, particularly in eastern England and the Midlands, where in some years it heads the list. The Common Shrew also favours rank grassland, and is more numerous when this is associated with woodland. Although the shrew is shunned by many predators because of its strong-smelling scent glands (Churchfield 1988), it becomes the main alternative prey in many areas; however it weighs only 5–13 g, and is not as nutritious in weight terms as the Wood Mouse or Short-tailed Vole.

The Barn Owl's breeding biology is largely geared to the availability of the vole, its main prey. It is not therefore surprising to find that when inexperienced young are attempting to find food for themselves in the autumn, the vole population reaches its annual peak. Wood Mouse populations peak later, in the early winter, whereas shrews tend to reach peak numbers in midsummer, with a rapid die-off in the autumn, and those shrews which do survive usually remain more hidden at this time, making them harder to find.

Changes in the numbers of these small mammals are often reflected by the variation in the owls' diet, so that shrews feature more commonly in the summer months, while mice often dominate in the winter. Diet is also likely to be influenced by the ease with which the prey can be found. In spring male voles become highly active in defence of their territories and shrews more vocal, while in the late spring and summer increasing vegetation may conceal certain species more than others. Wood Mice, for example, are often out on open fields of bare earth in late winter and early spring, feeding on drilled sugar beet and other seeds, while in summer, after the seeds have germinated, they retreat to the increased cover provided by the grassy field edges and woodland. Rats usually move to farm buildings in late autumn, when they congregate and become more obvious while shrews are thought to live underground more in winter, making it more difficult for owls to find them. The Mole is sometimes taken and, although its population may remain quite stable during the year, it is available only when active at the surface between May and August, presumably when the young are dispersing from their parental territories.

The House Mouse, which is about two-thirds the weight of its cousin, the Wood Mouse, is also found in pellets, but, in spite of the Barn Owl's reputation as a predator of commensal rodents, House Mice, like rats, rarely constitute a significant proportion of the overall diet in mainland Britain. Brown Rats are not often taken but can become significant locally in weight terms because they are much heavier than other prey items, even though the Barn Owl is usually able to take only the smallest and youngest individuals weighing 26–164 g. For this reason, it is only where colonies breed throughout most of the year that sufficient numbers of the right age class of animal are present for the rat to figure prominently in the Barn Owl's diet. The rat is, however, an important prey species in Ireland, where the Field Vole and Common Shrew are absent, and was also more common in mainland Britain before the 1950s when foodstuffs were stored in ricks and clamps. Barn Owls take advantage of these commensal rodents when opportunities arise: at a site I came across in Norfolk recently, for example, Barn Owls began egg-laying in February, two months earlier than usual and a second brood was produced in June. Pellet analysis revealed 82 per cent of the prey by weight was Brown Rat and 12 per cent House Mouse. The owls had confined their foraging activities throughout most of the year to the intensive rearing pens of a large bullock yard in which they were breeding. More often, however, rats and House Mice assume greater importance during winter months, especially in the cereal-growing regions of eastern England, where Barn Owls often vacate their tree sites in favour of warmer hay barns.

The Bank Vole is another small mammal commonly taken by the Barn Owl. This animal is restricted to hedgerow banks and woodland margins, but will occupy open grassland situations when the Field Vole is absent or in low numbers. Although I have described the Common Shrew and Bank Vole as less important prey species for this owl, both can be important in years when Field Vole numbers are low. The shrew can then assume major nutritional importance, especially in habitats which include coniferous plantations (in parts of Scotland and Wales for example), while the Bank Vole takes over in traditional farmland or parkland. The larger Water Vole is also taken in small numbers, particularly in parts of eastern England, although only young individuals are preyed on. I have nevertheless found a decapitated vole which, from an estimate of its jaw length, weighed more than 180 g. The Pygmy Shrew can figure in the diet of owls in quite high numbers in coniferous plantations, although, because of its very small size, it is nowhere near so important nutritionally. The Water Shrew is not common and as a result is taken only on very few occasions, as indeed are bats.

Communally roosting birds, particularly the House Sparrow and Starling, like commensal rodents, feature in the Barn Owl's diet more commonly during the winter, assuming major nutritional significance only during especially hard winters. In forest habitats in Scotland and Wales, young Meadow Pipits are sometimes preyed upon in summer. Very occasionally I have observed much larger species such as Magpie and Redshank being carried to the nest, although birds of this size are rarely taken.

The Field Vole and Common Shrew, two important prey species for the Barn Owl, Short-eared Owl and Hen Harrier in mainland Britain, are absent from Ireland, and the Bank Vole is only a recent colonist, first recorded in 1964. It has spread north, and can now be found throughout the southern half of the island. In southern Ireland it has been observed that the Wood Mouse and the Bank Vole occupy a similar open grassland niche to that of the Short-tailed Vole on the British mainland, although it is not known whether or not they can achieve the high population densities of the latter species in these open habitats. From my own very limited observations on the Isle of Man, however, from where the Field Vole and Common Shrew are also absent, I have observed greater densities of Wood Mice in open grassland situations than I have encountered in England. Throughout both Ireland and the Isle of Man, the Wood Mouse and the Brown Rat are the most important prey items in terms of nutrition for the Barn Owl. Pygmy Shrews, although only tiny, are taken in significant numbers in rural locations, and where the Bank Vole has become abundant in the south, it now provides 15–22 per cent of the diet by weight for Barn Owls (Small 1987).

Common Frogs are found in Barn Owl pellets more commonly in the spring, when they move to their spawning grounds. This amphibian could be important nutritionally if small-mammal numbers are low early in the year. When inspecting nestboxes in Scotland one year when vole numbers were low I found loosely bound 'golf-ball' pellets composed of the leg bones of frogs at some sites, and it was perhaps significant that brood size was far greater at these than at sites where frogs were not taken.

Insect remains are not commonly found in Barn Owl pellets, except in severe winters, when dung beetles and ground beetles are most usual.

Earthworms are rarely found in Barn Owl pellets in Britain. It is surprising that Barn Owls appear to reject earthworms, because they can be important in the diet of both Little and Tawny Owls.

Barn Owls do not appear to select voles, mice and shrews of any particular age or sex, but if, for example, large male voles are the most active in defence of their territories in spring and hence more easily available, they will appear more frequently in the diet at this time.

A typical male with pale upperparts and a wide white collar extending to the nape. The Wood Mouse is a very important prey item in agricultural regions of lowland Britain.

An unusual Barn Owl pellet, comprised entirely of frog bones. Frogs are often taken, especially at their spawning ground in early spring.

Barn Owl pellets are smooth-surfaced and usually larger than those of other species, appearing jet-black when fresh, drying with a surface glaze.

Tawny Owl pellets do not possess any surface sheen and are usually pale grey, irregularly shaped and powdery. They can appear brown and gritty which is an indication thay the owl has been feeding on earthworms.

Long-eared Owl pellets are relatively smooth-surfaced, having a slight gloss when fresh, while Short-eared Owl pellets are usually long and quite slender.

Little Owl pellets are small, their surface often glistening with the shiny wing-cases of beetles. They also feed on earthworms, when pellets appear brown and gritty.

Kestrel pellets for comparison.

Annual changes in prey

In the UK, small mammals, particularly the Field Vole, fluctuate cyclically with peak population densities every three to five years. Numbers fluctuate most widely in young forestry plantations and in grass moorland adjacent to coniferous forest. With the exception of those grasslands which are close to lowland, working farms, where a greater range of habitats can often attract up to eight different small-mammal species, the grass-moorland and forest-edge habitats normally support in addition to the Field Vole only two main species, the Common Shrew and the Pygmy Shrew, which, because of they are smaller, are of far less nutritional significance to the Barn Owl. In years of peak vole activity, Barn Owls occupying these areas will commonly raise large families and sometimes produce second broods. As vole numbers decline in subsequent years, and there is little opportunity to switch to alternative prey, the owls will suffer and either fail to lay eggs or produce smaller clutches and rear fewer young. For Barn Owls in upland habitats, occasional years of high productivity are therefore needed to maintain a viable population throughout the leaner years.

In lowland Britain, however, where over 90 per cent of the British Barn Owl population is found, annual breeding productivity is not so erratic. The birds are not so closely tied to the population cycle of a single prey species, because there is greater diversity of prey. In these habitats Barn Owls can adjust to the most readily available food such as Wood Mice, Common Shrews, Bank Voles, even House Mice and Brown Rats, and by so doing maintain a more stable breeding productivity year upon year.

In lowland habitats, however, climatic fluctuations can be major influences over productivity. In years of climatic extreme such as prolonged snow, continuous rain and drought, no matter how great the small-mammal diversity, Barn Owl populations experience temporary population setbacks. For example during the severe droughts which occurred in the summers of 1976 and throughout eastern England in 1991 and 1992, breeding output was badly affected. In these years the landscape in this part of Britain resembled semi-arid desert, with most of the rank grasslands reduced to almost bare earth. Not surprisingly, small-mammal trapping studies carried out in Barn Owl habitats in Norfolk and on the drainage banks in parts of Lincolnshire resulted in extremely low capture rates in places which would normally be teeming with voles, mice and shrews.

Food intake and body-weight changes

Feeding studies on captive owls are not a reliable guide to the amount of food a wild Barn Owl takes, as captive birds require far less less energy to find food, keep warm and defend the nest. Because it is not usually possible to collect all the pellets regurgitated by wild owls over the course of a full 24-hour period, the total weight of prey consumed is difficult to determine. Captive owls usually eat about 75 g a day, but it would seem more likely that the average daily intake for a wild bird would be more like 115 g. However this is likely to oscillate more than with captive birds, which are

Barn Owls often hunt from a perch in winter to help maintain energy reserves.

provided with their food daily and are not subject to the extreme environmental stresses experienced in the wild. I have, for example, found ten Common Shrews, and four Pygmy Shrews (120 g) in a single pellet and seven voles (140 g) in a few extreme cases in habitats where prey numbers are high. From this, it would seem that Barn Owls are capable of consuming much more than the 115 g daily average, assuming that these pellets represented one of only two meals eaten during the 24-hour period.

The two main times of the year when a good supply of food becomes critical are the pre-breeding and breeding period which includes the main period of moult, and spells of intense cold during winter. At both of these times, the demand for extra food increases, firstly to enable the female to put on sufficient fat reserves to produce and incubate eggs, and to grow new feathers, and secondly to maintain an increase in metabolic rate when temperatures decline. In winter, Barn Owls, like Kestrels, will hunt more often from a perch than on the wing. This can reduce energy, since, although hunting time is increased when waiting for potential prey to come within range, it is usually more cost-effective than actively seeking prey in flight. Although the chances of locating prey are greater on the wing, flight hunting is much more demanding of energy, particularly in cold conditions when metabolism has to increase simply to maintain body temperature.

We have only a broad idea of how energy requirements differ between males and females and how they fluctuate from season to season. Hens increase their body weight by about 50 g early in the breeding season to tide them over during egg laying, incubation and moult when they are unable to hunt for themselves. Cocks, on the other hand, maintain a slightly lower but fairly stable weight throughout the year, even though energy expenditure changes dramatically over the year, increasing in February and March during courtship and peaking with the huge demands made by the young in June and July. My own observations at nine nests, each containing four or five half-grown young, showed that 20–25 vole-sized prey items were delivered to the nest each night at this time, five to six times more than the cock would normally need to find for himself at slacker times of the year. Because he cannot put on reserves, he must instead increase his daily food intake to cope with these extra demands.

Energetics is better understood in the Kestrel than in the Barn Owl. It has been shown that a male Kestrel hunting five hours a day needs to eat about eight voles to maintain its weight, an amount considered the maximum it could possibly absorb in 24 hours. If it hunts for more than five hours, it has to rely on its energy reserves to maintain its efforts. Barn Owls, however, have only low fat reserves and could not rely on them for long, and thus a habitat consistently rich in food becomes essential.

The most profitable habitats offer large numbers of prey near the nest, and in the best Barn Owls have little trouble in breeding early, producing large and even second broods. At the other end of the scale, in territories where the main hunting ground is distant and prey numbers are low, the amount of energy expended will eventually reach a point where it matches or exceeds the total energy needs of the bird itself. In this situation the bird is no longer capable of delivering extra prey to the nest, and Barn Owls simply do not breed and are not found in such prey-impoverished habitats.

The silent hunter

The Barn Owl is known for its silent, floating moth-like flight along a hedgerow, open ditch or woodland edge. The flight path of an individual is predictable, and once it has left its daytime roost it will often follow a set route within its home range, deliberately to quarter an area of open grassland

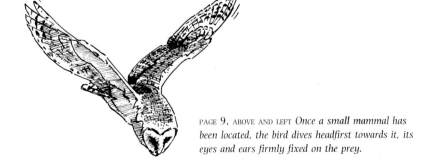

PAGE 9, ABOVE AND LEFT *Once a small mammal has been located, the bird dives headfirst towards it, its eyes and ears firmly fixed on the prey.*

Just before striking, the head is jerked back and the legs are raised, and feet and talons opened wide.

where prey is abundant. When *en route* to a distant hunting ground some Barn Owls will climb above the nest, flying high towards their chosen area. Its noiseless approach towards its prey is aided by the comb-like extensions on the leading primary feather and the fine end branches of the barbules (which produce the characteristic velvety sheen of the upperwings). These adaptations are believed to allow air to slip past and absorb any sound which would normally be created by the moving wings.

Aerial quartering When hunting the Barn Owl flies buoyantly, gliding about 2 m above the ground, stalling, twisting, cartwheeling and often hovering for a brief period before extending the neck and plunging arrow-like,

---

Once the prey is seized, the owl will often mantle it to protect it from the gaze of potential pirates and then feed on the spot.

Barn Owls will often hunt small mammals from the road surface,

head-first, towards its quarry. Just before striking, the head is brought up and the long legs reach forwards, feet spread for the final capture. Once the prey is caught, many Barn Owls will cover or mantle it with open wings to protect it from the gaze of other predators such as Kestrels and Carrion Crows, which I have often seen trying to take prey from Barn Owls. If the strike fails or is only partially successful, then the owl will sometimes skip along the ground for a few steps in pursuit of its quarry, and this behaviour is quite common among young birds, which have less experience of hunting. Once captured, the prey is eaten on the ground, carried to a nearby post, or grasped firmly in one or both feet and flown to the nest. If the prey is carried away, this is a sign that breeding is in progress nearby. If the prey is particularly large, the male will usually decapitate it first.

'Perch-and-wait' hunting Barn Owls will often hunt from perches, and some habitually do so. Like the Kestrel (Village 1990), this is more commonly observed outside the breeding season, particularly during heavy rainfall, snow or heavy frost, when energy is at a premium. At these times I have seen them sitting near the base of a hedgerow or in the branches of a spruce alongside the edge of a forest, where they are sheltered from the elements but are in a good position for alighting on any unsuspecting small mammal. Sometimes Barn Owls can be seen hunting from the surfaces of roads or tracks where small mammals cross in full view. Apart from the obvious hazards, this is probably quite an efficient technique and is one which has been observed in other parts of the world (Lenton 1984).

Bush-beating Another method of hunting is to fly alongside bushes or small trees, stalling and half-hovering on occasions while beating the small outer branches with the wingtips. This usually occurs at dusk in an attempt to dislodge roosts of Starlings, sparrows or thrushes and catch a straggler. As with perch-hunting, this technique is used more in winter, when large roosts congregate and ground prey can be more difficult to find.

Killing and eating prey Many owls appear to kill voles by a single bite at the back of the head, which is evidenced by a neat hole found at the rear of the cranium of skulls extracted from pellets. This is not always the case, however, as some skulls show no such damage; it is presumed that in these cases the animal is simply killed by the squeezing action of the feet. With mouse skulls, which tend to be more fragile than those of voles, the rear is inevitably shattered and it is therefore more unusual to retrieve intact skulls of mice from pellets. Perhaps with mice, which are far more active and jumpy than voles, the owl needs to deliver a number of blows to the head. Vole-sized prey is swallowed whole, head-first, but larger items such as Brown Rats, Water Voles, Starlings and even smaller birds are often decapitated and the wings of birds broken off at the elbow and discarded or the larger feathers plucked out. This is almost invariably so when the male is supplying the hen with food. The bodies, usually the forequarters, of large dissected prey are normally eaten first and the entrails are sometimes discarded. The skull and body remains will often turn up in different pellets, showing that these formed part of two quite separate meals.

Foraging times Barn Owl activity usually reaches a peak when the light intensity falls to a certain level, and it is believed that the bird's circadian rhythm is largely controlled by this. It is usually the case that Barn Owls will leave their daytime roost earlier when the evening is overcast and later on clear days. Bright moonlit nights tend to inhibit hunting and, courtship activity. At such times the owls do not venture out until the middle of the night, but perhaps voles and shrews, too, are influenced in a similar way and hunting success is therefore not much affected.

Activity patterns Barn Owls vary enormously in their hunting patterns in different parts of the country. Some will hunt during daylight in winter or summer, although this is almost always in late afternoon. Others are completely nocturnal except during times of food stress in winter or when feeding young. The Field Vole is active around sunrise and during the late afternoon, an hour or so before and after sunset, and it is perhaps not surprising to find that Barn Owls in parts of northern Britain and Wales which are largely dependent on voles for food are commonly seen in daylight, presumably capitalizing on these peaks of activity. In more restricted habitats, where the Tawny Owl is also largely dependent on voles, perhaps the Barn Owl's diurnal activity also helps to avoid competition from this more nocturnal owl, although it may also be a reflection of a low level of human activity in these areas which are usually more remote. For Barn Owls which feed more on mice or rats, which are mainly nocturnal animals, hunting by night is more likely to be the norm. Indeed, Barn Owls are less commonly found hunting by day in central and eastern England, where the nocturnal Wood Mouse features more prominently in the diet.

In south-west Scotland, which can suffer from days of continuous rainfall, diurnal hunting is particularly common after long wet periods, when the Barn Owl has had its hunting curtailed. In most habitats the owl's major period of activity is the three-hour period before and after sunset, when, on a typical evening, about fifteen returns to the nest will be made in the early to mid fledgling period when a brood of young is at their most demanding. Two or three returns are then likely until midnight, and then five or six in the next four hours until sunrise. Capture rates for one pair showed that on a dry, still evening the catch rate was one small mammal

Barn Owls are particularly vulnerable to fast-moving traffic when hunting roadsides.

every four minutes during the height of activity. This dropped to one every twelve minutes on windy days, and one every fifty minutes when it was both wet and windy (when there was more perch-and-wait hunting). During nights of continuous rain, no hunting was attempted but this invariably led to more daytime hunting the following day.

Chris Sperring has watched the way in which a male appears to select a particular area of the home range in which to hunt at a particular time. Once a feeding ground was chosen prey were brought in every four to eight minutes, suggesting that the owl had chosen a rich feeding area. The bird then switched to hunt in a less productive area, completely ignoring the first where he had so much success. The only conclusion was that he was deliberately not depleting the numbers of prey in any one area. I have also noticed that a breeding pair rarely concentrate their foraging activities in the prey-rich grasslands closest to the nest, because this is where the young will need to develop their hunting skills. It will, of course, assist the survival of the young if the prey remain in high abundance around the nest when they need planty of practice in refining their hunting skills.

Pellets

Barn Owl pellets are unlike those of any other bird of prey. When fresh, they are moist, jet-black and have a faint sweet musty odour. They dry into hard compressed pellets, with a fairly smooth and glossy surface. Their compactness, together with their hardened varnished surface, make them more difficult to break apart than those of other owls. Unlike other pellets they are not powdery, and the fur that binds the intact bones appears to undergo little change during digestion and is easily identified. As pellets age, they commonly attract a number of species of clothes moth. The maggot-like larvae with off-white bodies and orange heads consume fur within the pellet before pupating and emerging as adult moths which escape, leaving what look like narrow transparent brown tubes radiating like antennae out of the pellet surface. As the pellet ages and becomes subject to the ravages of moth larvae, it becomes more fragile and eventually begins to fall apart. Pellets which are found in damp or wet situations appear less likely to attract moths, but their surface is often dotted with a range of brightly coloured moulds of white, yellow, orange, red, blue or green.

Large accumulations of Barn Owl pellets along with copious amounts of 'whitewash' usually build up at nest sites or daytime roosts. When entering a barn, the first thing to look for is signs of white streaks of droppings on an overhead beam or ledge. Because birds of prey regurgitate a large pro-portion of undigested waste material, their droppings are very liquid and normally do not contain any black solids, unlike those of most other birds. If the streaks are long and have dried, particularly at their ends and usually on the ground beneath, into a thick cream-coloured, chalky deposit, they can usually be attributed to a bird of prey. If 'whitewash' is present, then a careful inspection of the ground beneath will usually reveal anything from one to scores of pellets, depending on whether this is frequently used as a daytime roost or nesting site or as a temporary night-time stopping-off place. Pellets found in semi-enclosed buildings will often be those of Barn Owls, but Kestrels, Little Owls and Tawny Owls also use these places. To the trained eye, the shape, consistency and size of the pellets, even if partially fragmented, will usually confirm which species has used the building. Barn Owls roosting or nesting inside tree cavities, however, rarely advertise their presence in this way, and it is quite uncommon to find noticeable signs of 'whitewash' around the rim or beneath the entrance hole. Pellets, too, are more difficult to find at tree sites, since most are cast within the chamber itself and the elements soon destroy those that might otherwise be found under a roosting branch (where chalky-white droppings can often be found). Before leaving this subject, it is worth warning that Barn Owls seem very accurate in their bombing, usually selecting an escape flight path directly overhead and shooting a stream of smelly 'whitewash' over any unsuspecting survey worker, who invariably has only just put on a clean shirt! While this may be a consequence of the 'flight-and-fright' reflex mechanism common among animals, part of which seeks to expel any waste products to lighten the load prior to fleeing, I am becoming increasingly convinced that in the case of the Barn Owl it is primarily used as a defence mechanism.

Barn Owl pellets can vary in size, but they are similar in both shape and size to a man's thumb, slightly larger in diameter at the centre than at their rounded ends. If a bird has had a particularly large meal, it produces a longer pellet. With these larger pellets, although the end which emerges first is rounded, the other will often have a distinct taper or 'tail', which presumably is the result of the drag on the end of the pellet in the oesophagus as it is regurgitated. Pellets can measure up to 120 mm long, but they normally average 42 mm long by 26 mm wide.

Sometimes, pea-sized pellets are present among accumulations which, because they can be found outside the breeding season, cannot always be attributed to a young bird. They occur most commonly during periods of severe winter weather when hunting has proved difficult, but can also be found alongside equally fresh normal-sized pellets, suggesting that they were residual remains. Indeed, they sometimes contain the single skull of a vole or mouse, which may indicate that the owl had decapitated the prey and consumed the rest of the body at some other time.

Other unusual and very large Barn Owl pellets found on one occasion in Lincolnshire revealed almost entirely vegetable material, particularly grass. They were hard and impossible to soften in water, and resembled black pitch; I would not have considered them to be those of a Barn Owl had they not been found at a traditional roost and contained some evidence of unbroken vole and shrew remains. Certainly, there was nothing to suggest that the owl had been trying to feed on earthworms, and I have never been able to ascertain the reason why these pellets were almost entirely composed of vegetable remains.

Because Barn Owl pellets from different individuals are usually similar in diameter, presumably determined by the size of the owl's oesophagus, pellet length can provide an indication of the amount of live prey which has been taken. Michael Toms, however, has found a more reliable way of determining the number of prey items or live prey weight using pellet volume, which is derived from the mean width and length. The exception is when wet pellets drop from a high beam onto a hard floor: they dry into distorted dumpling-shaped mounds, making calculation more difficult.

Digestion The extent of bone digestion in predators varies between species and is dependent on the level of chemical activity in the digestive tract. In the owls (which do not possess a true stomach), the resting acidity level in the forepart of the gut where digestion occurs is between pH 2.2 and 2.5, about the strength of vinegar. In diurnal birds of prey, however, such as falcons and eagles, it is normally much stronger with a pH of between 1.3 and 1.8 closer to the strength of concentrated hydrochloric acid.

Because diurnal raptors tear up their prey before swallowing and possess high acidity levels, although the teeth of their victims often remain partially if not wholly intact, they digest most of the bone they consume, making it more difficult to identify remains.

The degree of bone digestion can vary between a hungry owl, which might have higher levels of acidity, and one digesting a previous meal. During very severe winters I have found at some roosts copious liquid tar-like deposits mixed with wet pellet fragments, which may have been the result of prolonged retention and more complete digestion during periods of food stress when there would have been little opportunity to find a new meal.

Before pellet ejection the bird becomes rather sulky. After a time it drops its head and shakes it from side to side, the beak is opened and closed as the movements in the oesophagus bring the pellet into the mouth and it is disgorged. Pellet ejection is usually stimulated by the immediacy of the next meal and is considered a conscious action. It has been shown with captive Barn Owls that the sudden appearance of the keeper, whom they associate with food, can immediately induce pellet ejection, provided that the last meal had been eaten at least six hours before. It is generally accepted that Barn Owls produce about two pellets a day. Since Barn Owls commonly concentrate their main hunting activity in the evening and early period of the night, this would suggest that the nightly pellet is cast during the early morning just before setting out for another meal about 7–8 hours after the food was swallowed. If the stimulus for pellet ejection is the immediacy of the next meal, then the pellet resulting from the morning meal may be retained for up to twelve hours, or longer during the long days of summer. This might suggest that the bone remains in daytime pellets are more digested than in night-time ones, although I know of no evidence for this.

Immature owls may digest bones more thoroughly, although I have seen no obvious signs of erosion to skull or limb bones in pellets from nest-boxes, which contain hundreds of prey items most of which would have been produced by the juveniles. If significant digestion of bone does occur in young owls, it does not seem to change the appearance of the main ones.

It is also said that remains in owl pellets do not necessarily provide a true yield of the number of prey consumed, because some bone digestion occurs. With captive owls fed on day-old chicken chicks, in which mineralization of bone is incomplete, there can be a noticeable thinning of the skull bone in pellet remains. If the numbers of wild prey are assessed in terms of the largest and most sturdy bones, such as the upper skull or jaw, however, this usually provides an accurate picture of prey consumed. If this assessment, however, is based on the numbers of pelvic bones, for example, it can often lead to an underestimate because some dissection of even small prey items occurs, with the front half of the body seemingly favoured.

Pellets are therefore important to the owl researcher and can provide reliable information about prey preferences, including the age, structure and sex ratio of small mammals that are taken. Age can be determined from the amount of tooth wear or the jawbone length, and the sex from the shape of the pelvic bone. Analysis of pellets can also reveal animals hitherto unknown in the area, which can be very useful for mammalogists investigating the distribution of species. For example, the Hawk and Owl Trust is conducting a research study covering Lincolnshire which embraces a number of habitat types. Pellets are being collected from the same roosts every eight weeks over a period of five years in an attempt to determine any seasonal or annual fluctuations in the prey being taken as a means of understanding why the birds are so successful in this intensively farmed county. So far the project is only into its third year, but marked seasonal and annual differences have already been found.

Barn Owls usually regurgitate one pellet at their main daytime roost in late afternoon or early evening just before hunting. Large numbers can build up at these sites. Large accumulations in buildings can indicate that the Barn Owl is nesting there, but in other cases they simply reveal that it is a favoured roost. A second pellet is usually cast during the night at one of the stopping-off roosts in a building or beneath a post or tree.

6

TERRITORY AND TERRITORIAL BEHAVIOUR

Breeding season

Many non-migratory birds spend most and sometimes all of their time as breeding adults in a small area or home range. Clearly, home ranges are rarely neat circles around the nest, since the suitable habitats within an area are rarely homogeneous. In eastern England, for example, where a large majority of the terrain comprises vast prey-impoverished agricultural land, Barn Owls depend almost entirely on the linear grassland edges along ditches, rivers and field margins. Here, home ranges can often be lozenge-shaped, with birds ranging greater distances for food than their counterparts in traditional or more confined grassland habitats.

When we speak of a home range of a Barn Owl during the breeding season of about 3 km², this reflects the average size in most habitat types within which catching prey and delivering it to the nest remains efficient. In winter, the size will commonly increase in response to a declining food supply. This expansion becomes possible because, unlike in the breeding season, the bird requires food only for itself and no longer needs to devote enormous energy to hunting and carrying large numbers of prey to the nest.

Some birds defend their home range rigorously against both their own species and others, and in this situation it is more commonly referred to as a territory. The Tawny Owl is particularly aggressive in defence of its territory in mature woodland. The Barn Owl, however, is not territorial in this sense, and, while it will defend the immediate area of about 5–10 m around its nest site early in the year and during much of the nesting period, its foraging range will often overlap with those of adjacent pairs. Although birds of different pairs rarely hunt together in the same field, I have on a number of occasions observed two or more different males, each of which were busy feeding young, hunting within 50 m of the other without any serious challenges.

It is unclear whether or not Barn Owls use natural landscape features to determine the limits of their home range. They are nevertheless remarkably consistent in their movements commonly following natural boundaries such as roadsides, ditchsides and hedges en route to their chosen hunting grounds and often conducting display flights along them.

Throughout Britain and Ireland, 49 per cent of the 10-km squares contain one or more breeding pairs of Barn Owls and population levels in these squares range from approximately one to thirty pairs, although 99 per cent fall within the range of one to nine pairs. On average, the population density is about 2.5 pairs in each occupied square, which is only one every 40 km^2 some ten times less than that of the most populated square in Britain and one hundred times less than found in some Malaysian oil-palm plantations.

The greatest Barn Owl density in Britain I have actually recorded is 27 breeding pairs within an area of 100 km^2 in south-east Yorkshire, which is equivalent to about one pair for every 4 km^2. In south-west Scotland where the Hawk and Owl Trust erected large numbers of nestboxes in farm buildings, the population density within a single 10-km square in 1991 (a high vole year), was 21 pairs, with a further five occupied sites during the same year in barrels placed in trees by the Forestry Commission. Even in the following year, when vole numbers fell, eighteen pairs were present and it seems likely that numbers may be increased still further as more sites are provided in this region over the next few years. Densities much higher than this can, however, occur. In Malaysia, for example, they exceed 250 pairs in each 10-km square in some oil-palm plantations where ample food is available and large numbers of artificial nest sites have been provided. Here, the distance between neighbours is less than 200 m, and it is possible that with more nest boxes owls could nest even closer given the high abundance of prey in these plantations. In the 1800s, when food supplies were probably much better than they are today, owleries were described in Britain in which at least thirty to forty Barn Owls were found occupying a collection of cottages with interconnecting roof spaces (D'Urban 1895). Other reports have alluded to over a dozen owls with young at a single breeding site in the roof of a country house (Mathew 1894). I, too, have first-hand evidence of three females all producing young in the same farmhouse roof in Sussex in 1984. Communal nesting has also been described from France (Baudvin 1975) and America, and in Africa large numbers of Barn Owls will nest very close together, taking over the massive stick nests of the Hammerkop, where home ranges become indistinguishable from one another. Collectively, these observations reinforce the fact that the Barn Owl appears weak territorially and is quite capable of achieving high densities when food supplies are rich. In Britain, however, even where nest sites are in good supply, prey levels rarely achieve those found in these countries, and for this reason population density is much lower and home ranges tend to be well separated.

The Barn Owl, although not so sedentary as the Tawny Owl, rarely moves far from the nesting site it has chosen in its first year of life. Even when food supplies are threatened because of cyclical changes in numbers of its favoured prey or following severe habitat destruction, it usually remains faithful to its chosen home range or does not stray far from it. Within the home range are found, as well as the main foraging places, the nesting site and a number of well-used roosting sites, the most secure of which will usually be used for breeding if the traditional nest site becomes unsuitable owing to disturbance or loss or when a second brood is attempted.

Winter

Unlike the situation with the Barn Owl in North America (*T.a. pratincola*) and in parts of Europe (*T.a. guttata*), where long-distance movements of up to 2000 km can occur in response to sudden winter adversity, Barn Owls in the UK usually maintain their traditional roosting sites throughout the year, rarely moving far from their favoured hunting grounds. Nevertheless, foraging ranges can increase in winter from 1–2 km from the nest to 4–5 km (Cayford 1992). This is presumably because suitable foraging habitats become more patchily dispersed as vegetation dies back and small mammals seek the shelter of field margins and farm buildings, where they become less accessible to Barn Owls. In eastern England, for example, particularly in parts of Lincolnshire, East Yorkshire, Norfolk, Suffolk, Cambridgeshire and Bedfordshire, the number of days of annual snow cover is greater than anywhere else in lowland Britain. In this flat landscape, Barn Owls hunt the drainage ditches and the wide grassy verges of the quiet country lanes. Here, snow is whipped up by the winds to accumulate on the north-facing banks of the ditches, while the south-facing banks are usually left comparatively free and what does settle rarely lingers long in the warming sun. Even though some grassland remains free of snow, these conditions effectively reduce hunting opportunities within the normal home range, tempting the owls further afield and closer to farmsteads, where hay barns and other farm buildings offer extra food and shelter. In other areas, such as the exposed moorland regions of Scotland and Wales, where snow cover can be prolonged, the mature conifer forests come to the rescue, providing the necessary shelter on their south-facing edges from the falls of snow which would otherwise accumulate here. It is often these small microfeatures of the landscape that finally prove so important in determining whether or not Barn Owls are able to survive and maintain their breeding numbers in these otherwise bleak and hostile regions of Britain. It is perhaps not surprising to find some extension of the bird's hunting range during winter, and although it is more likely to over-lap with those of other Barn Owls at this time of year its apparent lack of territoriality means that this rarely seems to result in any major conflicts.

7

VOICE

Bunn, Warburton and Wilson, in their excellent monograph (1982), have described the Barn Owl's voice in depth, and I have taken my account partly from theirs but supplemented it by my own listenings and those of Chris Sperring, who has mastered many of the Barn Owl's calls and is able successfully to call them using his own voice.

The Barn Owl is largely silent from July to January, and, contrary to popular belief, does not hoot. I should like to have been given a pound for every time I have heard people say that they have Barn Owls on their farm because they hear them hooting at night. On investigation many of these do indeed have Barn Owls, but the almost inevitable presence of Tawny Owls with their more vocal nature leads to much confusion.

The calls of the Barn Owl, as those of many birds, are made for good reason: either to proclaim its territory (by singing) or to attract a mate, as well as to maintain contact with one another. It seems difficult to associate the Barn Owl's shrill and rasping screams with its courtship song, especially when compared with the melodious singing of other groups of birds such as thrushes and warblers or the wonderful wavering hooting of the Tawny Owl, but that is precisely what it is. The Barn Owl has a range of different calls at different times of the year, all of which mean different things. Although the bird has a wide repertoire, I have attempted to group these calls in a logical sequence from courtship through to the independence of the young, incorporating the different alarm calls at the end.

Courtship

The screeching song The Barn Owl is famed in legend and superstition for its screeching song, which chills even the most experienced listener. Both sexes utter this call, which can only be described as a long drawn-out tremulous screech increasing in volume and then finishing quite abruptly. The tremulous effect seems to be caused by the movement of the bill, which is clearly perceptible when watching a bird calling at rest, but it is possibly enhanced when in flight by the regular rise and fall of the wings and chest cavity. The screech is most commonly heard in the very early months of the year while the pair is in courtship flight over open grassland or along a forest ride not far from the future nest.

The male's screech has a higher pitched and more cleanly delivered pea-whistle tone than the female's and is best described as 'sshrrrreeeee'. As well as being uttered in flight, the screech is also used by male birds, especially those attempting to attract mates, from a high vantage point such as the apex of a barn roof, often at or very close to the site the male regularly uses or near to the one which in past seasons has traditionally been used for breeding. The screech usually lasts about two seconds and can be uttered either many times in succession during courtship chases or just singly when patrolling the territory. It can carry tremendous distances, much further than the songs of other British owls, and I have heard it almost 1 km from aviary-confined owls on a still overcast night. Sometimes a subdued single screech may be given at dusk at other times of the year when the bird leaves its roost, but I have heard this on only a few occasions.

The female almost always screeches when engaged in courtship flight and when being pursued by her screeching partner, but it is given less frequently than that of her mate. Her screech is slightly longer than the male's, lower-pitched and more broken or tremulous, dropping off in tone and volume at the end. It is perhaps best described as 'sshrreee-eeoo-o'. At certain times during courtship this call can break into more of a wailing clearer tone, not dissimilar to the sound of wailing cats.

Greeting chirrups and twitters The cock almost always advertises his presence when meeting his partner with a squeak and a series of airy chirrups and twitters, especially when delivering or offering food at the nest. The female often greets the male with a similar repertoire, but again this is distinctly louder and of lower pitch. Chris Sperring has used this call successfully to summon wild Barn Owls which had already been drawn in quite close by the screech, with the result that it encourages them to come in very close indeed, when they display a great deal of head movement. This seems to confirm that this call is used as a means of establishing or maintaining contact and in recognition when the partners are already close to one another. It is also commonly used during allopreening. Young owls will also use these calls when in the nest or when close to their parents.

Copulation squeaks This greeting, an almost submissive call uttered by the male, will burst into a frenzied plaintive and stacatto squeaking during the period of copulation, which is often prolonged and sometimes lasts up to 30 seconds or so. The female at this time will purr and snore excitedly.

Food-begging snores This begging or hunger call is usually uttered by the female (and later the young) and is perhaps the most commonly heard Barn Owl vocalization. It is best described as a wheezing or rasping hiss, varying in length and repeated persistently, and can be mimicked by sucking in air sharply through pursed lips. It usually occurs when the female has the male alongside and, because it is in essence a juvenile call, it stimulates him to move off and seek food. She will also use this as a contact call when answering the male as he flies past the nest site soon after egg-laying, when they are roosting apart. Later in the year the female will use it in a similar way to encourage the young to return to the nest to be fed, and after this to draw them out of the site when they are learning to catch prey. Because they continue to associate this call with food, it is not surprising that it also acts as an effective contact call at this time.

The young regularly use this hunger call. When they are very young the snores are weak and irregular, reminding the parents of their presence, but after about ten days or so it becomes most persistent when they are hungry and stimulates the male to bring food. In the first few weeks of their development it is distinctly less throaty than that of the female and almost always longer in duration. This call can carry quite long distances on still nights, making many an unsuspecting farmer explore his hay barn to find the 'man of the road' he believes is shacking up asleep and snoring loudly – is actually a group of owlets lined up on a beam!

Bonding churrups and chitters This is a fast churruping made by the hen, similar to the greeting call. It is used at the nest just before the eggs hatch, when the young can also clearly be heard calling inside their shells, and is probably used to establish the first contact between mother and young. It is also used by the hen when toying with food in the nest, probably to remind the young that food is available at a time when they are still blind. The young also make a similar but higher-pitched chittering during the first three weeks of life. This seems to be used when exploring the nest, seeking attention (especially if the hen leaves the nest area), or expressing discomfort (particularly if the young become chilled, when it stimulates the female to begin brooding).

Defence and distress

Defensive hisses These are used to frighten enemies, usually when threatened at the nest, and are similar to food-begging snores but longer, shrill, louder and more explosive, almost approaching the screech in tone and volume. The hiss is repeated over and over, ending in a whistle as the breath runs out, and it becomes more and more frantic the closer danger comes.

Defensive clicks This often accompanies the hiss and can be described as a loud sharp-sounding click. It is used by adults and often by well-grown owlets, usually when they become very agitated or aggressive. Because of its volume this sound is thought to be caused by the tongue being sucked into the pharynx, rather than by the actual snapping of the bill. Although the bill certainly closes as the sound is made, it seems that the first explanation is probably correct because it is easy to imitate by drawing air into the mouth and sucking strongly with the tongue pressed hard to the palate.

Distress volley This volley of loud explosive screams with a cat-like quality, usually delivered at the nest and beginning with the defensive hiss, signifies extreme fear, and I have heard it on one occasion when two birds were locked in battle, one of which I suspected to be of captive origin.

Anxiety screams A piercing, plaintive scream commonly used by the male as he arrives at the nest to warn the female or young of danger.

Alarm squeal This is a high-pitched squeal or scream of alarm or warning directed at an adversary and uttered while in flight. I have heard it most often during daytime when birds have seen me near a nest with young. Once, they launched themselves at me from the roof of an old cottage where they had young, enraged at my presence. If, on the other hand, the male is surprised while hunting, for example, the squeal is more subdued and shorter and seems more an expression of surprise.

Mobbing yell This call is usually delivered as a loud shrill screech by a stationary bird and is angrily yelled often at a ground predator. Newly fledged owlets use a version of this in an attempt to see off intruders.

8

SOCIAL BEHAVIOUR AND DISPLAYS

Aggression

Because Barn Owls are not highly territorial, defending only the immediate area around the nest, conflict is quite rare either between individual Barn Owls or with other species. Confrontation does occur close to the nest, and I have seen aggressive encounters between Barn Owls as well as between Barn Owls and Kestrels when one has violated the airspace above a well-established nest site. On the three occasions I have witnessed this between two Barn Owls, once in Scotland and twice in eastern England, the resident bird appeared out of the site, meeting the potential aggressor head-on in flight, uttering the alarm squeal followed by the loud distress volley of screams. Both rose in the air breast to breast, locking talons, tumbling a metre or two and then disengaging, after which the intruder flew swiftly off, pursued unrelentlessly for a short distance by the

This defensive display is commonly used in confined places such as nest sites, when the female cannot escape and must intimidate her attacker into retreat.

screaming territory-holder. This can sometimes result in death, as the puncture marks on the breast of two autopsied birds confirmed where conflicts between two individuals had been observed prior to death. On a number of occasions when a Barn Owl needed to cross over the main hunting area of another bird Chris Sperring has witnessed extraordinary behaviour. The first bird would rise high above the nest on a thermal until it was almost out of sight, fly over the disputed territory and then stoop suddenly like a bullet in the manner of a Peregrine with folded wings to begin poaching on his neighbour's land. Chris has also observed this high stooping behaviour by a Barn Owl which was being harried by a gull for the vole it was taking to the nest, the speed of the stoop leaving the gull floundering in its wake. Bob Sheppard has seen a Kestrel try to take a vole from the talons of a Barn Owl which was flying towards its nest, and this was such a violent assault that the owl fell tumbling into a bramble bush and had to be helped out. This was not an isolated occurrence of piracy, and there are quite a number of reports of Barn Owls and Kestrels attempting to remove hard-won prey from one another when the temptation arises. Sometimes this has involved the Kestrel flying at the owl, turning over on its back and grabbing the vole from the owl's talons, while at other times the Kestrel has attacked from behind. Nevertheless, the two species are normally very tolerant to the extent that they will frequently nest alongside each other without any noticeable adverse consequences. In Lincolnshire, one of my two-tier nestboxes on poles had Kestrels in the upper compartment and Barn Owls in the lower, and in straw-stack sites this is not a particularly rare occurrence, (and in two instances Little Owls shared the stack as well!).

Defensive displays

When approached at their breeding or roost site, female Barn Owls will usually slip out in advance of the intruder, generally on the blind side of the building, and I am sure that the owls, given the choice, commonly choose buildings with more than one entrance and exit to enable them to achieve this. When on eggs or brooding very small young, hens will normally sit tight or move into a hidden corner nearby. In more confined sites however an adult will threaten an intruder, taking up a forward threat attitude much different from that of other owls, by ruffling the body feathers and crouching to the ground while straining forward with bowed head and wings spread horizontally as if almost toppling forwards. The head swings from side to side, and the whole performance is accompanied by short hissing and tongue-clicking with the bill open. This can turn into more prolonged hissing with the bill closed, increasing in volume and vigour and often ending up in the distress volley of loud cat-like screams. Body-swaying and sudden forward lunges are accompanied by deep bows while trampling the feet. I have seen this posturing at a site when well-grown young were approached by a Stoat, which was able to snatch one of the weakest youngsters unable to put up much resistance. Barn Owls, especially young birds which are in confined spaces, will commonly retreat,

Barn Owls are not birds of woodlands but will commonly hunt their grassland margins or nest in boxes placed around the edge of mature conifer plantations.

to the rear of their nestbox, for example, lean rigidly backwards and attempt to strike aggressively with the feet and talons. If the threat appears from above, they will lie over on their back for support, enabling them to direct more punch into the strike. When picked up, Barn Owls commonly play dead. This trance-like state can be induced in an active owl by turning it on its back and gently stroking the back of its neck, after which it can usually be laid out stiff and rolled over, appearing completely dead; but it can quickly come to life, suddenly flying away as if nothing had happened.

9

BREEDING

The breeding cycle involves a number of distinct but continuous phases from early courtship to the eventual independence of the young. This cycle is especially long in the Barn Owl and can be attributed in the main to the prolonged fledging period, which for each owlet usually takes 55–65 days.

Because incubation begins soon after the first egg is laid, asynchronous or staggered hatching occurs. This can commonly result in at least eight days' difference between the youngest and the oldest in a brood of four, and as much as thirty days in some situations. The brood occupies the nest for about seventy days, but this can be much longer when the laying period has been especially prolonged. During years when prey is readily available and the climate relatively mild, courtship will normally begin in February or March, at which time male voles are beginning to show themselves and become more mobile in defence of their territories, the time in the year when they are most easily found and caught by Barn Owls. The first egg is usually laid in the first or second week of May (average date 9 to 12 May), with birds in south-east England and south-west Scotland generally being a week or two earlier. In young conifer plantations clutches are often laid in late March or early April, which is probably a reflection of the owls' high dependence in this habitat on voles, which, when at high density, often challenge their territories early in the season.

My figures suggest that in Britain and Ireland as a whole 4.9 eggs is the average clutch size, but this can vary between years depending on the availability of prey, so that in one year it can be three and in another as many as nine. The first chick hatches during the first or second week of June, which in most years coincides with rising vole numbers. By the second week of July the young are half grown, and in the third week of August the oldest owlets are fully fledged and begin to leave the nest site – when Field Vole numbers are reaching their seasonal peak. The long-term average number of young that fledge in Britain and Ireland is 3.0, but, like clutch size, this varies regionally, with Barn Owls in south-west Scotland and south-east England, which laid earlier, rearing more young (Percival 1990). Throughout Europe as a whole fledging success increases from north to south, with birds in Britain producing 3.0 young and those in parts of southern Germany, France and Switzerland between 4.4 and 4.5. By mid to late September most of the young have become independent of their parents and disperse, firstly to sites nearby and then further afield.

The entire breeding cycle takes five-and-a-half to six months, during which time the food requirement increases from about ten vole-sized items per pair in 24 hours (115 g per individual) to 30–35 items (700–800 g) during the mid fledging phase, assuming a brood of four. Although fairly impoverished habitats are potentially capable of supporting a single Barn Owl in the non-breeding period, during the breeding season food needs are massively increased. It is therefore only in those habitats which are capable of delivering much higher quantities of food that breeding will take place and where Barn Owls are still to be found. The different stages of the breeding cycle are now discussed in more detail.

Early courtship

It is not an easy matter to investigate the process of pair-bonding in wild birds. Barn Owls will breed at between ten and eleven months of age, although males are sometimes found breeding for the first time in their second year. In captivity, however, I have known successful breeding to occur at 26 weeks (female) and 34 weeks (male). In cases where breeding in the wild occurs late in the year, or where individuals of second broods do not achieve independence until early winter, this does perhaps demonstrate that even these latecomers which are eventually recruited into the breeding population are capable of breeding in their first season at less than ten months. What is clear is that the Barn Owl has enormous capacity to raise large and multiple broods where food supplies are rich and climates are mild, highlighting an important aspect of the bird's breeding biology which is unmatched by any other British bird of prey.

Barn Owls are usually monogamous, selecting another mate only when one of the pair has died. Among those pairs which have survived intact since the previous breeding season, some will roost away from the nest site, sometimes apart, not returning to the nest until the early months of the new year. Members of other pairs will join up towards the end of the previous breeding season, usually in July or August, and remain at their breeding site all winter. In exposed habitats, Barn Owls which strive to maintain their nesting sites in hollow trees during the winter are commonly forced to move into hay barns to roost between the bales when temperatures fall during frosty nights or when food supplies become low. Those using exposed nestboxes in open barns or trees will also move into these warmer sites. Barn Owls seem particularly vulnerable at such times, and their behaviour suggests that the defence of their future breeding site takes second place to ensuring that they can maintain body temperature and minimize energy expenditure at a time when body reserves are at their lowest level. This does, however, pose the risk of losing a potential breeding site to other hole-nesting species, particularly Jackdaws, which can be tenacious in their attempts to occupy tree cavities as well as nestboxes, which, once filled with sticks, become of little use to Barn Owls. Tawny Owls, too, because they are early nesters, have the opportunity to take over sites temporarily vacated by Barn Owls during cold spells in early winter.

Serious courtship usually begins in March, although pairs which have not maintained their traditional nest site over the winter will often arrive in February and begin screeching while flying in and around the main roosting sites, one of which will be chosen for nesting. At this stage the male also begins patrolling the favoured hunting areas, momentarily stopping to hover as if in an attempt to make his presence known. For single birds whose mates have not survived the winter and at newly provided sites such as nestboxes, it is usually the male birds which arrive first to advertise their presence, often uttering their screeching call from the top-most vantage point of a nearby building. At traditional nesting places where the female has maintained her breeding site throughout the year but has lost her mate, I have found that she has managed to attract a new partner to the site, and one can only assume that she has done the wooing. In some instances a widowed female can be found occupying a different breeding site with her new mate, although this is rarely far away from the first.

Once a pair has been established, the male bird will continue to perform short flights around the main roosting sites and then move off to conduct wide circuits within a radius of 1–2 km, as if patrolling the limits of his home range. Flights at this stage are often slow and hesitant, when the owl will stall and hover momentarily without any serious attempt to capture prey. Eventually, the female will join the male and the two perform more energetic chases, turning, twisting and weaving in and out of the different roost sites and across the adjoining fields. At this time they are both very vocal, the male with his high-pitched tremulous screeching and the female with her somewhat lower-pitched, hoarser and slightly extended screech. I have witnessed very few serious challenges with rival Barn Owls during these courtship flights, but most of my observations have involved pairs which maintained their sites all winter or were in regions of low popu-lation density. There may indeed be more aggressive encounters between individuals attempting to occupy new sites or in places where populations are higher and competition for nesting places greater. I have nevertheless witnessed this on one occasion when a male flew over an established nest site, whereupon both birds rose up together in the air like fighting cocks, locking talons and then separating instantly, with the intruder making off at great speed and the aggressor screaming in brief pursuit.

During courtship flights the male will often pursue the female from above, chasing her through the potential nest site in an open building, or into the branches of the chosen tree, when the first attempts at copulation are made. As courtship progresses the male often emerges just before dusk, flying aggressively out of the site, climbing high into the sky and then returning at great speed into the site. He will eventually reappear and fly away to begin hunting. At this time the female usually emerges to take up a vantage spot on top of the building or on a branch above the nesting chamber, where she preens. After a while she will suddenly disappear into the nest site and this flurry of activity signals the arrival of the male with food, at which time the first attempts at copulation are sometimes made.

Often, the period between the female diving back into the site and the male arriving is anything from one to two minutes. The actual time lapse is often very predictable at certain sites, which suggests that the male must utter some contact call (audible to the female but not to me) at the far reaches of his hunting territory to signal his return with food. I have also noticed a similar sudden change of behaviour with young birds, which predictably begin snoring lustily for food a minute or two before the male returns with prey; this again suggests that some form of contact call is uttered. Food-caching by the male is common at nest sites during courtship, and is probably important in stimulating the hen to allow copulation and for reinforcement of the pair-bond in general.

Late courtship

The female becomes less active as egg-laying approaches, when she is fed almost entirely by the male. Chris Sperring who has conducted intensive work at a number of nest sites and has has provided me with some of his observations, is able to predict when breeding is about to commence from the pellet remains: when the percentage of shrews in the diet falls to below 30 per cent in numerical terms and the more nutritious vole takes its place, this invariably signals the beginning of egg-laying.

The hen usually utters begging snores at this stage, similar to those produced by young Barn Owls. This often prompts the male to hunt more actively, and he will usually return with food soon after. If the snoring call fails to elicit any response, she begins a soft purring call; this is usually sufficient to encourage the male to present food, at which time copulation normally occurs. This involves the female crouching low with the tail extended skywards, whereupon the male mounts, grasping the female by the nape feathers. Copulation itself, which takes about 15–20 seconds, is normally preceded by the male presenting the hen with prey from the food cache, which is often quite substantial at this stage. The food item is often held by the hen throughout the act of copulation, which occurs repeatedly each evening for weeks prior to, during and even after egg-laying. This is usually preceded by mutual allopreening and followed by general lethargy. As egg-laying time approaches, the female becomes progressively less active, decreasing her hunting effort and remaining close to the nesting site. She is now dependent entirely on the male for food, which enables her to maintain and build on her energy reserves.

Egg formation demands a great deal of energy and additional protein, and as a result the female's body weight increases from about 335 g in January and February to 385 g by April or May. This weight change coincides with a further decrease in the activity of the hen, who becomes tied to the nest and reliant on increased provisioning and food-caching by her mate. Once maximum weight is achieved, egg production begins and the necessary reserves are in place for incubation and moult. Severe weather conditions during the period leading up to breeding can have a profound effect on its timing and eventual success, particularly if these conditions involve long periods of lying snow, heavy frost or rainfall.

Sufficient food-provisioning by the male is therefore critical during this time when the hen becomes reliant on her existing reserves and on the prey caught, delivered and stored by the male. Food caches are probably important for the male to be able to guarantee a constant food supply to reinforce the pair-bond when bad weather could curtail hunting or cause him to be away from the nest for long periods.

Nesting

It is generally believed that Barn Owls make little attempt to construct a nest, although eggs are usually laid on a pile of pellet debris, but it is not uncommon for the female actively to shred pellets and for the eggs to be laid on this prepared carpet. On one occasion I also watched a male spending some time trampling pellets before placing a dead vole on to the debris, where the eggs were eventually laid. This does not, however, seem to be a necessary prerequisite for successful breeding, since Barn Owls will lay their eggs directly on to clean wooden boards on a hay-loft floor, for example. In these situations pellets inevitably accumulate when the hen is on the nest and it is not uncommon to find that the female has drawn them in around her so that she becomes surrounded by a neat halo of pellets, which may serve to reduce heat loss but provide no actual cushion. At one new nestbox site in south-west England, Chris Sperring found that the female prepared the nest carpet three weeks before eventual laying, but because she was disturbed by young heifers which were suddenly allowed into the barn she vacated this site, laying almost immediately in an alternative nestbox nearby directly on to the wooden base, presumably because there were no pellets available in this new box for shredding. The final outcome was a large brood of eight, all of which fledged, so the fact that her eggs had no cushion seemed to have no adverse effect. It is possible that breeding sites with little evidence of pellet debris may be those which were occupied in an emergency, since it is quite unusual in my experience for Barn Owls to nest at a site which has not previously been used for roosting and where pellets have not had a chance to accumulate.

Eggs and incubation

Barn Owl eggs are chalky-white, bantam-sized and more elliptical than those of other British owls. They are normally laid on alternate days: a clutch of five eggs would take about nine days to complete. It is not wise to try to determine precise egg-laying intervals because of the risk of disturbance at this critical stage in the breeding cycle which can prolong the laying period. In some cases a long interval of six days or more can occur between eggs, particularly when spells of bad weather prevent prey deliveries to the nest, which, unless a good store of food has been laid in, reduces opportunities for copulation and can also lead to infertile eggs being laid among fertile ones.

In the British Isles, clutch size can vary considerably from two to nine eggs although the average is five. Large variations can, however, occur with the same birds between years, particularly with those in more marginal habitats such as grass moorland or upland areas where the Field Vole is the most significant small mammal. Here, pairs may lay two or three eggs in years when voles are scarce and eight, nine or more when they are abundant. In captivity, one pair was reputed to have laid 26 eggs, of which 21 were fertile, in 62 days. This demonstrates the Barn Owl's enormous breeding potential, but in the wild, even in the best feeding conditions, the numbers which eventually hatch will ultimately be dictated by how many the female is capable of covering during incubation. Although eight and even nine young are occasionally reared in the wild in Britain, this is probably the upper limit for a single brood even in the richest of habitats.

A recent study has shown that large numbers of prey visits, averaging sixteen a day, can occur during the laying period, which appears far in excess of the female's needs (Langford and Taylor 1993). From my own experience this is the one time when the cock actually feeds at the nest, which he will occupy with his partner throughout the egg-laying period. Filming at the nest has also shown that the male will arrive with prey, pass it to the female, copulate, and then take back the food item, leave the nest and then return with it on his next visit to copulate again. All this demonstrates the importance of food presentation in the copulation ritual. Nevertheless, food will accumulate at the nest at this stage, acting as a cushion for the hen against bad weather and sudden prey shortages at this critical period when egg-laying drains resources and there is a constant need to replenish and maintain reserves in preparation for moult and the long incubation time ahead.

Once the clutch is complete, which can take anything from eight to twenty days and occasionally longer, the male begins roosting and feeding away from the nest. The proximity of this roost is probably dictated by the availability of suitable structures in the area, but, as I have explained before, it is always close to the nest itself and sometimes in the same building. In derelict cottages, for example, where the female typically nests under the roof or in a blocked chimney stack, the male will often be found

Barn Owls do not construct a nest as such but will often lay eggs on a cushion of pellets which she will sometimes deliberately shred.

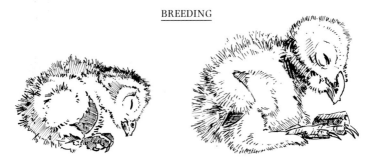

The sequence over the next few pages shows the development of a young Barn Owl from hatching to near-independence. Once it has dried out after hatching, the Barn Owl chick has a fine layer of down. A week later, it is strong enough to raise its head for short periods and can use its wing stumps to move around the nest.

in the other chimney at the opposite end of the building. If a suitable roost is unavailable this close to the nest, the male often chooses a stand of trees adjacent to the old building. In the Lincolnshire fenlands, where the only available sites in some areas are pairs of boxes erected on poles, the male will often occupy one while the female will nest in the other. The apparent dependence on a suitable roost in close proximity to the nest may be a critical factor governing the eventual selection of the nest site itself. The male will actively begin to cache prey at his roost, and should any prolonged disturbance occur near the nest which inhibits his prey deliveries, then this food is temporarily stored here.

When leaving his nearby roost, the male will fly past the nest site uttering an almost imperceptible version of the chirruping contact which his partner will answer with a hunger snore, after which serious hunting begins. About eight or so prey items are delivered daily to the female during the incubation period, which for each egg is 30–31 days.

Hatching

The young can clearly be heard chittering in the egg up to two days prior to hatching, at which time the female becomes highly excited, constantly shifting her position and churruping loudly and excitedly. Hatching can take 48 hours as the chick attempts to chip away with the small egg tooth on the upper surface of the bill, assisted by the hen who will tap on or even help break the shell to encourage the youngster out, after which she delicately removes the shell fragments Once out of the egg the chick develops rapidly, and the shells are removed or in some cases partially eaten by the female. The eggs hatch at staggered intervals dependent on the laying interval, usually about every 48 hours, but, as I have mentioned before, this can vary enormously, with the youngest and oldest in a brood being separated by up to thirty days or even more.

In a year when prey is abundant and weather conditions are good, most of the eggs which are laid will normally hatch. Taking a ten-year average from my combined records in Scotland and East Anglia, the hatching success is 75 per cent. On hatching, the young are pink-skinned

This picture clearly shows the effects of asynchronous hatching. The owlets here range from one to four-and-a-half weeks old.

The quills of the wing feathers start to appear at 14 or 15 days, and the chick opens its eyes for short periods. By 21 days the mesoptile plumage has formed, and the eyes are fully opened. At 28 days the facial disc feathers are visible and the eyes are turning from milky-blue to brown.

At about 35 days the owlet nears its maximum body weight of about 400 g
and will clamber around near the nest. A week later the facial disc has formed,
although not all of the feathers are fully grown. At about 50 days, the tail
feathers are longer than the primaries and the owlet can make its first attempts
at flight, and by 56 days it will be following its mother around the vicinity of
the nest site and learning hunting techniques.

with large potbellies, measure about 50 mm long and weigh 14 g. The closed eyes form protruding lumps on the side of the large head, and the bill, which is an ivory colour, possesses a tiny egg tooth on the top of the beak. A few hours after hatching, the chicks dry to reveal greyish-white down which covers the upperparts and the front edges of the tarsus and toes, although the sides of the neck, the belly and the back of the tarsus are almost bare. At this age the owlets utter a faint chittering call. This is most commonly heard when the female briefly leaves the young to defecate or when she is receiving food from the male, which she will then tear up. She then straddles the young, dangling a small morsel of meat in front of one of them which, once the meat touches the bristles around the base of its bill, hurriedly takes it and swallows it. For the first week or so the hen does not feed any roughage but just the soft parts; these can often include pieces of intestine, and because of this no pellets are produced at this stage. The male continues to copulate when he arrives with food, and in confined spaces this takes place while the hen is crouching above the eggs or small young. This makes them especially vulnerable and may account for a greater failure of eggs at natural sites than in nestboxes (boxes are usually spacious, allowing the hen to move aside when the male arrives).

Growth of the young and parental care

Throughout the first week the owlets' growth is rapid, and for the first two days or so they are able to gain nourishment from the yolk sac. The neck soon becomes stronger and the owlet begins to hold its head up, although only for very short periods. The legs also become noticeably stronger, which results in more movement around the nest As prey is delivered, the chittering develops into the more characteristic snore in response to the food-offering call of the female, and the droppings which are deposited are eaten by the hen.

During the second week the first owlet to hatch becomes noticeably stronger than its nest mates and begins to use its wing stumps to move more rapidly around the nest. Because of the rapid body growth at this time, when the young put on about 12 g each day, the down is no longer able to cover the body and the chick has a very bald appearance. Its eyes open for short periods from about the twelfth day, after which it begins nibbling at prey items and pellets begins while uttering a rapid chittering note. Loud hisses and tongue clicks are also heard when the nest is disturbed. Towards the end of the second week fine quills are apparent, which quickly give rise on about the thirteenth day to the second white down, after which rudimentary attempts at preening begin. The egg tooth usually falls off at this time. At this stage the owlet is able to hold itself upright, although the eyes still remain open only for short periods.

At the start of the owlet's third week, on the fourteenth or fifteenth day, it usually weighs 200 g and is already halfway to attaining its maximum body weight. At this stage in its development the primary quill tips are just becoming visible. The owlet now begins to snore lustily when the adult arrives with food, which it is now capable of swallowing whole. With wings raised and tail wagging, it is now able to move backwards.to the edge of the nest before defecating. By the end of the third week the second white down is long, thick and almost fully developed, and the primary quills and facial-disc feathers can be seen clearly, although the eyes remain blue and misty. By now a surfeit of prey has often accumulated around the nest, but the female will only leave the nest for short periods to defecate nearby.

By the beginning of the fourth week, the weight gain of the oldest chick begins slowly to drop off and the amount of prey being brought in to the brood is close to its maximum, averaging twenty vole-sized small mammals every day. I have, however, recorded as many as 33 similar-sized items being delivered to a family of six owlets in 95 minutes at one prey-rich site on Anglesey where the youngest was three weeks old. On about the twentieth day, the primary wing quills are clearly visible with down at their tips. By the twenty-fifth day the primary quills are 2.5 cm long, the tail quills begin to unfurl, the claws begin to lengthen and the eyes begin to turn brown. When disturbed, the owlet will turn over on its back with feet raised in threat. The hen usually vacates the nest about this time when all the young are able to swallow whole food themselves, usually roosting well away from the nest at her own site. She will commonly bathe after leaving the nest and eventually begins to hunt and deliver prey to the nest, although the male still continues to be the main provider. Neither parent stays at the nest for long, usually spending just enough time to deposit the prey. On two occasions at this stage in the young birds' development I have watched sites where one of the adults has been killed by a vehicle. In both instances the remaining bird was able successfully to raise most of the young to fledging.

By the beginning of the fifth week, weight gain has fallen to 4 g a day and the amount of prey being delivered to the nest begins to fall off. On the thirty-first day the primaries are about 7.5 cm long, displaying about 2.5 cm of the unfurled feather, and the facial disc is developing fast. The owlet is very active at this age, snoring loudly when hungry, flapping its wings and wandering beyond the nest. The nest becomes very soiled, with an accumulation of large pellets and copious droppings collecting around the edge.

By the middle of the sixth week, when it is around 37 days of age, the owlet has usually achieved its maximum weight of about 400 g, which is significantly greater than that of its parents and after which prey deliveries to the nest become less frequent.. When awake the owlet snores and preens constantly, although it still sleeps for long periods flat out on its stomach.

At the start of the seventh week the facial disc has formed, although the white stiff feathers which eventually cover the cere up to the forehead have not fully grown at the midline. The primaries are now about 12.5 cm long, and the down is being shed rapidly.

By the start of the eighth week the tail feathers extend beyond the primaries, although some down is still present on the tops of the legs and on the belly. It is at this time that the first attempts at short flights are usually made.

Leaving the nest

By the ninth week the owlet has trimmed down to about 335 g and looking very adult in appearance, can often be distinguished only by its exaggerated head movements. The oldest owlets now begin to leave the site to explore the immediate area, chasing one another in and out of the site and nearby buildings and screaming loudly at any human intruders. At this stage they follow the hen around with prey or sit on fence posts close to the nest, often ending up in the long grass chasing imaginary prey. On arriving with food, the female will usually present it to one of the youngsters only if it follows her back to the nest site, and this behaviour persists until all of them are capable of flying. The male, on the other hand, arrives at the empty nest to leave the food and continues to have little to do with the young.

Training the young

By the start of the tenth week the growth of the wing feathers is almost complete, and the hen starts to train the youngsters to find and catch prey. She will circle with food in her feet, flying high above the nest site and snoring loudly to draw the youngsters out into the open, where they will flop into the grass or fly beneath, calling in anticipation. Once they have gathered, she drops the prey and there is a scrabble to catch it in mid-air. Invariably the food falls to the ground, and one or more of the young hovers above or dives down into the grass, running trying to find it. Chris Sperring has watched a female flying above 'a perfect pyramid of eight owlets' which cascaded like a display team after the food was dropped.

The first prey capture by the young owls is not normally made until the end of the tenth or eleventh week, at which time the first pure screech is often heard. At this time the adults, which are by now often roosting together again away from the nest, are rarely seen, although the young remain conspicuous and continue to be tolerated by the parents unless one of them attempts to enter their own roost site. At this stage the owlets are highly vulnerable, and it is quite usual in Scotland to see them sitting out in torrential rain or stranded in long grass. They end up chilled, water-logged and lethargic, and commonly die of starvation and cold, which I am sure must be the most significant cause of natural mortality in the high-rainfall regions of western Britain during September and October, when high mortality occurs in young Barn Owls. By the end of October, the surviving young are usually capable of finding all the food they need and they slowly begin to depart from their natal site, some temporarily taking up roosts nearby and others dispersing further afield.

Food consumed during nesting

Removal of the total pellet debris from a nestbox in which eight young had been reared to fledging revealed a total of 1398 skulls and seven uneaten prey items. Identification of the skulls gave 93 per cent voles, 3.5 per cent mice and 3.0 per cent shrews. Since the nestbox was entirely clean before the first egg was laid, this indicated that, over the 93 days from the first egg until the young became independent of the nestbox, the minimum average daily prey weight consumed by the hen and her eight young was 40g for each individual per day: in other words, a total prey weight for the brood and hen over this period of 32 kg, and for the family as a whole, including the male, equivalent to around 2000 vole-sized prey items. A particularly interesting observation at this site – and it may happen elsewhere, too – was that when the pellets were collected from the cock's main roost over the same period, they were found to contain a completely different prey spectrum from that which he had delivered to the nest. Unlike the nest, which held 93 per cent voles, the pellets at the roost contained 82 per cent shrews and only 18 per cent voles. It seems very unlikely that the male would hunt selectively, but what is more probable is that he actively chooses to consume the smaller and less nutritious prey that he catches consistently providing the largest and best to his mate and her young. This would enable him to keep the number of excursions to the nest to a minimum thereby saving on energy expenditure, since, in weight or nutritional terms, for every three Common Shrews he needs to provide only a single vole. This may also tie in with Chris Sperring's earlier observations, when he maintains that he is able to predict when the female is about to lay because the male switches from bringing in a mixed prey spectrum of voles and shrews to one composed almost entirely of voles.

Site fidelity and incestuous mating

Barn Owls maintain a very strong and intimate association with their chosen breeding sites, many of which are of great antiquity. Old diaries of farmers show that some have been occupied for well over a hundred years and certain very ancient tree sites have been used for much longer periods of time by successive generations of owls. Traditionally used nest sites are usually vacated permanently only when the surrounding land is unable to provide sufficient food because of serious changes to the habitat, or when the nesting site or adjoining roosts themselves have been modified or destroyed. Once the home range has been selected and successful breeding takes place, it is very rare indeed for either of the partners to move in subsequent years even following major habitat upheaval or the loss of the nest site itself. If for any reason the nest fails in the first year, however, the site is rarely used again although the birds will breed nearby in subsequent years if suitable alternatives are available.

   In spite of the Barn Owl's highly sedentary nature, it is probably uncommon for mating to occur between close relatives such as parents and offspring or between siblings. In most cases, young animals generally disperse away from their natal so that inbreeding is less likely. It is interesting therefore to find that incestuous matings between Barn Owls have been reported in recent years. One involved a pair of juvenile birds believed to have been reared from the same parents, the female coming from a first brood and the male from a second; the other case involved an incestuous mating between a mother and her son when he was a year old (Anderson

1989; Shaw 1989). In 1993 an even more surprising event was reported to me from Lincolnshire when two siblings bred successfully at the same nest in which they themselves were reared (and ringed) the previous year. We have little knowledge of how often incestuous mating occurs in Barn Owls, but it would seem more likely in small fragmented populations which are striving to maintain viability and where the opportunities for finding unrelated partners are few. Nevertheless, the instances alluded to above were in areas of high population, so the reason for this occurring is not so easily explained, and there may also be some advantage in inbreeding to maintain or reinforce what has become a successful local trait.

Bigamous mating

Polygamy is rare in the Barn Owl. I have only come across it when there has been a rich food supply around the nest sites in question. In one instance, a single male was feeding two females nesting inside a single building in south-west Scotland, one with four full-grown young and the other with a single four-week-old chick. It also occurred at the same site two years later, when seven owlets were raised from two adult females which were being served by a single male. At another site in southern England, three females were tending young within the same roof space of a very large hip-roofed farmhouse; two of these were consistently being fed by the same cock bird, but both males always left to hunt in different directions, one on a pig farm and the other over open grassland nearby. Bigamy seems to be especially common with Barn Owls which were originally released from captive stock having successfully adapted to the wild. This would be understandable if they were being supplemented with food, but in most instances they were into their second, third and fourth breeding seasons. Perhaps the initial isolation of many of these released communities and the lack of any wild Barn Owls in the release areas tend to encourage this type of behaviour.

Breeding failure and second broods

Complete failure of Barn Owl nests is uncommon. When it does occur, it is usually related to prolonged periods of wet weather or seems to be triggered by thunderclaps, or by repeated human disturbance, particularly during the early egg stage. Repeat clutches will be laid, but I have never known this to take place at the same site if the birds have previously failed there nor for the site to be used again while one of the pair remains alive. Second clutches, i.e., those laid after the success of the first, probably occur more frequently than previously thought particularly in rich habitats and in year of high small-mammal abundance. If the adult pair are present at a nest with well-grown young then this is a good indication that a seond clutch or brood is imminent (normally adults roost away from the nest at separate roost sites).

On many occasions the second clutch is laid in a different place from the first, sometimes within the same building or in another one nearby.

Where nestboxes are in good supply the birds often switch to an adjacent box to rear the second brood, and when boxes are positioned in pairs both can be used by the same female during the same year. The young from the first clutch are often still in the nest when egg-laying begins for the second time, and in some cases they will remain with the female even though a new site has been chosen. Normally, second broods are not so successful as first broods, and it is not unusual for only one or two young to be reared or for complete failure to occur.

The effect of supplementary feeding

In an attempt to assess the effects of food supply on the eventual breeding success of Barn Owls, I conducted a number of studies at wild nests where the birds were provided with supplementary food in the form of dead day-old cockerel chicks. Five pairs of Barn Owls which had regularly nested at their traditional farmland sites for many years were chosen for this investigation. Previous studies at these nests had revealed that the five pairs had successfully raised young on sixteen occasions over the past four seasons. The average laying date for the first egg over this period was 4 May, ranging between 14 April and 20 May. The average clutch size was 4.9 (range 4–7), and the fledging success was always good at between 3 and 5 (a precise average could not be determined because some visits were mistimed during some years).

During 1991, three day-old cockerel chicks were provided every second day from early January, at the time when one or both adult owls were occupying the nest site. At two of the sites, pairs were in residence all year. Supplementary feeding was discontinued when egg-laying commenced and resumed for five weeks following completion of the full clutch and during the period of early brooding. The average weight of the food provided for each pair was 1200 g before egg-laying and 875 g during the period of brooding. It was not possible, however, to be sure if all of this food was delivered to the female, even though it was provided on a secure feeding ledge at the place where the male alighted on entering the building. Although I never observed anything to the contrary, some food could have been cached or taken away and eaten by the male.

What effect, then, did the extra food have on the breeding success of these birds? There was a slight increase in clutch size from 4.9 to 5.6, but no significant difference in the eventual fledging success, which averaged 3.6 and ranged from 3 to 6. What was particularly noticeable, however, was that the date of the first egg had advanced dramatically by an average of 35 days, with dates ranging from as early as 27 February to 12 April and a mean date of 30 March. Even more interesting was the fact that four of the five pairs laid second clutches, all of which were successful in fledging young. Three of the second clutches were laid at an alternative roost site in a nearby barn rather than in the original nest building, although one pair laid eggs alongside the first brood when the oldest was five to six weeks old. In the entire four-year period prior to this supplementary-feeding experiment, there had been no double-brooding attempts made by the owls at these sites and it could not be argued that this was an exceptional year for Barn Owls generally in the area, because five other pairs in similar habitat nearby fledged an average of 3.2 young, with a mean first-egg date of 1 May, none of which produced a second brood.

In summary, supplementary feeding prior to egg-laying and during incubation and early brooding led, in this experiment at least, to a slight but insignificant increase in clutch size, and fledging success, but a major advance of four weeks in the laying date, and the production of second broods by four of the five pairs. The first three of these observations were similar to supplementary-feeding results for wild Sparrowhawks (Newton 1986), although this experiment with Barn Owls led to a much greater advance in the laying date. Supplementary feeding finally resulted in a significant increase in the average overall fledging success of these five pairs, from 3.1 to 5.4 young per pair, over two broods.

It is known that in captivity Barn Owls given unlimited food will sometimes lay larger-than-average clutches, although they usually fledge about three to six young. Once again, the main effect, however, is on the timing of egg-laying, which is commonly one to two months earlier than for wild pairs and it is not uncommon for two and sometimes three clutches to be laid each year. This can also happen at sites where the owls have been reintroduced and where supplementary food is continuously provided even in situations where the birds are capable of catching sufficient prey for themselves. In Malaysia, two and sometimes three wild broods are not uncommon in oil-palm plantations, where rats are always abundant and where ten or more young are often reared every year.

It seems likely that eggs are laid as soon as the female achieves a critical breeding weight. In the wild, the female begins to lose weight at the nest as her reserves become depleted during egg-laying, early moult and brooding. If her initial increase in body reserves is maintained by the provision of large quantities of food through the early breeding period, this appears to be the trigger for the production of a second clutch. Had I chosen sites in more marginal habitat, where the number of eggs laid would normally be lower than the average, it is possible that I would have noticed a more significant increase in the number of eggs laid as well as an increase in the young that were fledged from the first brood.

Shortage of prey is undoubtedly the main factor limiting breeding success in the wild today, and it may prevent Barn Owls from rearing sufficient numbers of fledged young to offset the annual mortality rate. Although the supplementary feeding of wild pairs in spring can lead to an increase in the numbers of young which fledge, this technique should not necessarily be seen as a recipe for trying to increase the breeding population. Nature is usually finely tuned such that the numbers of Barn Owls which eventually survive into adulthood to breed are finally determined not by the amount of artificial food provided early on, but by the

The male brings food to the female on the nest, and will then copulate. During incubation she will turn the eggs repeatedly. She will tear off small bits of prey for young chicks, while largers chicks may undertake whole prey items.

Hilary Burn

amount of wild prey available once they leave the nest. In other words, while it may be possible to double the fledging success artificially, once the young leave the nest nature may act simply by reducing the numbers which survive into adulthood in line with what the habitat is able to support.

Supplementary feeding in severe winters may well have some conservation value. Much as with the increased overwintering survival of small garden birds resulting from the hand-outs of peanuts on birdtables, the provision of food for wild Barn Owls in winter can help them to maintain breeding condition and reduce mortality and this is often demonstrated by those involved in the reintroduction of Barn Owls. Supplementary feeding of wild owls is probably very little different from what was occurring in the stackyards of yesteryear. Although these were not specifically designed by man to offer prey-rich pickings for Barn Owls they were probably crucial for artificially maintaining the breeding populations of a bird otherwise unsuited to food shortage in harsh winters in northern climes.

Factors affecting breeding success

The overall breeding success of a population can be measured in terms of the numbers of pairs reaching breeding age and achieving breeding condition, their clutch size and hatching success, and finally the numbers of young birds which eventually fledge from the nest.

Because Barn Owls are specialist feeders on small mammals, any sudden or indeed long-term change in the numbers of their prey can have a profound impact on their reproductive success, and should the change be part of a long-term trend then this can influence their population level. It has long been accepted that Field Vole numbers fluctuate in a cyclical manner, and that Barn Owls and other birds of prey which are largely dependent on this small mammal are governed by these fluctuations. Sometimes the annual changes in vole numbers can be massive, and in some study areas they have been shown to vary from five to 1000 voles per hectare, and exceptionally to 3000 per ha.

Although a number of researchers, especially those working with birds of prey, have investigated the changes in vole numbers in their own study areas, and have established a period of three to four years between peaks, no long-term study in Britain has been conducted to provide any annual measure of vole abundance at a national level.

For the Barn Owl, however, figures are available which allow us to get some measure of annual variation. Since 1909, records of the numbers of Barn Owls ringed have been supplied to the Ringing Scheme of the British Trust for Ornithology by experienced ornithologists. By 1931, the totals ringed were differentiated into adults and nestlings in the records, and these were becoming sufficiently large to allow valid interpretations to be made regarding annual changes in population. One way of determining these annual changes is to divide the number of young Barn Owls ringed in any one year by the total number of all Barn Owls ringed during that year. This figure, known as a 'ringing or population index', can be used to compare Barn Owl numbers from one year to the next. When these indices are plotted for the years 1931 to 1992, a picture emerges which shows that Barn Owl numbers reach a peak and a trough regularly every three to four years. Sometimes the peaks are very noticeable, as in 1943 and 1972, suggesting years of very high Barn Owl productivity, while in other years they are especially low, as in 1957 when no Barn Owl chicks were ringed. This index can provide a comparative guide for distinguishing between years of maximal and years of minimal productivity and the frequency of these peaks and troughs. The results show that numbers have fluctuated rhythmically over a mean period of 3.4 years since 1932. Although similar indices do not exist for voles in Britain over the same time period, it is generally accepted that both fluctuate over a similar three-to-four-year period. Ever since Field Voles were found to fluctuate cyclically in this way, mammalogists have been trying to identify the underlying cause, and many theories, including reduced food supplies, predation, parasitism, social behaviour and genetics, have been proposed. Although there is increasing evidence that these peaks and troughs occur over large areas, biologists are not much closer to finding the true causes of this biological phenomenon.

Climatic influences

Climate is the fundamental natural influence governing a species' population, by regulating the availability of food and shelter. The climatic extremes associated with snowfall, rainfall and drought can affect the breeding productivity and survival of Barn Owls and influence their population level, either in a temporary way or in the longer term.

Barn Owls are dependent not only on the absolute numbers but also on the availability of small mammals for their breeding productivity and overall survival. It would be of little use, for example, having plagues of small mammals if they lived in dense woodland, high-standing crops or beneath snow where they were hidden from view. While some owls of the extreme north such as the Great Grey Owl are capable of plunging through deep snow to capture prey, the Barn Owl, with its origins in the tropics and more temperate climates, is not suited for this type of capture.

Snow cover Since the Barn Owl is at the limit of its world breeding range in Britain, severe winters are likely to have a serious inflence on its numbers. I analysed the meteorological records of snow depth and duration from figures provided from low-lying stations in the different regions in the British Isles since 1932. Although the number of days of snow cover in any one winter did not imply that snow had necessarily lain continuously over this period, it provided a valuable comparative annual figure for the length of snow duration over the last 60 years. From these figures it was possible to construct a graph, similar to that of the ringing index, for the average number of days snow lay on the ground in any one winter from 1932 to 1993. Barn Owl numbers were at their lowest in those years when snow duration was greatest. This finding was highly significant in statistical terms, with twelve of the cycles showing a direct correlation, suggesting that Barn Owl numbers were strongly influenced by the availability of small mammals and not solely by their actual numbers.

While it is also probable that the breeding success of small mammals themselves is affected in severe winters, in spite of their being able to survive under deep snow, the real reasons why their populations suddenly decline on a three-to-four-year cycle are still not known. Nevertheless, whatever the underlying cause of this phenomenon the Barn Owl population has consistently declined to its lowest temporary abundance after winters when snow duration was greatest, and this has been evident since reliable records of Barn Owl numbers first became available in 1932.

Since my own investigative analysis (Shawyer 1987), a new study has been undertaken which was able to test this hypothesis (Percival 1990). It was reassuring to find that, although it used a different set of data, this latter study confirmed that there was a significant relationship between breeding productivity and survival of Barn Owls and the degree of snowfall and low winter temperatures, which collectively determine the duration of lying snow. This investigation also demonstrated that high summer rainfall was significant in reducing breeding success, something which I, too, had identified, particularly during the wettest years this century in 1946 and 1958, when Barn Owl productivity reached an all-time low in Britain.

In Britain, winter snowfall is usually heaviest and most prolonged during the first three months of the year. Over the last thirty years, snowfall has on average been most prolonged is the last week in February, which also happens to be the time when Barn Owls usually begin court-ship. In order for the males to attract mates or strengthen the existing pair-bond, they need to convince their would-be partners that they have selected a rich and productive habitat where prey is freely available. During this courtship phase the male attempts to achieve this by delivering prey to a potential nesting site, caching it and eventually presenting this food to his mate, which is the trigger for copulation to begin.

The ability of the female to gain weight rapidly from February onwards is probably crucial if egg-laying is to commence at the optimal time, in April or May. If food is in short supply because of severe winter snow (or sustained rainfall), however, then the male is often unable to find sufficient prey to bring his mate into full breeding condition. As a result, breeding may not commence at all that year, which is what happens with Tawny Owls, or, more commonly with Barn Owls, it is delayed until the female achieves her necessary reserves. Should breeding be delayed following early months of snow or heavy continuous rainfall, it is usual for Barn Owls to produce smaller-than-average clutches, resulting in fewer fledged young. This is because the young from late clutches leave the nest in early winter, when prey populations are in decline.

Continuous rainfall Continuous rainfall, like prolonged snow cover, can affect the timing of breeding and overall success. Rainfall, because it is not simply a winter phenomenon in Britain, can cause problems through-out the entire breeding season up to the time the young are seeking independence. Although some birds attempt to 'still-hunt' from sheltered perches, this method of inactive hunting rarely results in enough captures to satisfy food needs at a time when demands are particularly high. Barn Owls observed hunting in relatively light rain have been shown to have capture rates some ten times lower than those they can achieve in the same field in dry conditions. In addition, the activity of small mammals themselves can be inhibited during wet weather, and the acoustic clues they normally provide to hunting owls can be suppressed in saturated grasslands.

Long periods of rainfall and the lack of sufficient prey being delivered to the nest can encourage the female to move away from the nest, resulting in incomplete fertilization, egg-chilling or starvation of young. It has been reported that cannibalism within broods can be associated with the food stresses brought on by heavy rainfall (Baudvin 1975) or high atmospheric pressure and thunderclaps (Shawyer 1987).

Heavy rainfall can also reduce overall breeding success, especially in September and October, when the inexperienced young are leaving the nest site and are attempting to gain independence. Juvenile Barn Owls are often found dead or stranded in long grass at these times, saturated and chilled, and this seems to be the most common natural cause of juvenile mortality in the late autumn, particularly in western districts, and may account for a significant proportion of deaths in the so-called 'unknown catagory' in my mortality studies where Barn Owls were simply reported as 'dead in field'.

Drought Unlike the previous climatic extremes of snow and rain, drought at its most severe, such as those events experienced in parts of Britain in 1949, 1976 and 1991, does not hinder the Barn Owl's ability to hunt but probably reduces the numbers of small mammals, particularly Field Voles, which favour open grassland habitats. The sudden loss of grass growth and increased grazing pressure from cattle at such times is likely to lead to the migration of small mammals into field margins, resulting in a decline in their numbers as a consequence of increased competition for food. Drought, when it occurs to this extent in Britain, is likely to be most felt by Barn Owls in summer and autumn, when young are in a more advanced stage of development or at the time of their independence.

Regional variation The significance of each of these three climatic extremes on breeding success and adult mortality is undoubtedly influenced by the type of habitat that Barn Owls choose to occupy. It is likely that in the strongholds of Cornwall, Wales and south-west Scotland populations will be influenced more by the effect of rainfall, which is very high in these western regions of Britain, than by snow, which is for the most part light. In eastern Britain, in the strongholds of East Anglia, snow cover is likely to be the main climatic factor influencing productivity and survival, since annual rainfall here is only half of that of western Britain. Snow duration increases not only from west to east in Britain but with also altitude, and this, too, is a factor governing the Barn Owl's breeding success and ultimate survival in those places above 150 m, which are as a result considered marginal for this bird in Britain.

10

MOULT

The regular replacement of feathers is necessary if birds are to maintain their powers of flight and insulation against the wet and cold. Owls, more than any other group of birds, are dependent on silent flight and manoeuvrability to outwit their quarry. Their hunting ability would be seriously impaired if they were to lose large numbers of flight feathers all at once. For this reason many diurnal birds of prey moult individual wing feathers over a period of months, even though they replace most of their feathers every year. With the Barn Owl, however, moult is especially prolonged and is not completed until the bird is around three years of age, having taken two full years from beginning to end.

The production of new feathers is a highly demanding process, requiring extra food in order to derive protein and increased energy. At this time, the skin develops large numbers of blood vessels at its surface from which the growing feathers are fed with proteins and other nutrients. Because the blood has closer contact with the outside, this can lead to problems in maintaining body temperature. Moult therefore places great strain on metabolism, and as a result is usually timed to coincide with a period during the year when food is plentiful and when there is less need to hunt and maintain body warmth.

Primary moult

Most of the information on the Barn Owl's moult is from studies conducted in Germany and Malaysia (Lenton 1984), but here I have supplemented these with some of my own observations from Britain. Barn Owl primary wing feathers have usually attained their full length at about eight to nine weeks of age. After about ten to thirteen months of age, during the bird's second calendar-year, moult of the primaries begins. This usually occurs between late May and October for females and a little later, between July and October, for males. Females therefore begin their moult to coincide with the time they have attained their maximum body weight and during the most inactive period of their lives, in May and June, when they are incubating eggs and brooding small young in the nest. Clearly there is a great advantage in moulting at this time, because this is when females are largely dependent on their partners for food, where there is little need to hunt and when body warmth is easier to maintain within the confines and shelter of the nest. By the time the female begins to leave the nest to resume hunting after about seven weeks of incubation and brooding, moult has usually ceased and the female is now at her lowest weight, having lost about 50 g. The male could probably not afford to begin his moult as early as May or June, because this is a time of intense activity when mating occurs regularly and when the female and young are dependent on his increased hunting ability to provide them with sufficient food. Collectively, these two activities require massive energy demands. Male Barn Owls therefore usually begin the moult in late July or August, after the female has left the nest and is able to assist in the feeding of the young. This is also the time when the young owls have achieved maximum weight and their food demands are decreasing.

Many birds, including most members of the Strigiformes, shed their primaries in a regular sequence beginning with the inner one and ending with the outermost, with all feathers being replaced every year. The Barn Owl, the Snowy Owl and Great Horned Owl, however, begin their primary moult with the central feather. Feathers are then lost sequentially in opposite directions from this feather inwardly (descendently) and outwardly (ascendantly). Moult of the primaries in Barn Owls of both sexes usually involves the shedding of just one of the ten main primary feathers, usually the central one (number 6), from both wings between May and October, when the bird is a year or so old. There is then a cessation of moult until May–October of the following year (third calendar-year), when the bird is two years of age. At this time four primary feathers, usually numbers 5, 4, 7 and 8 (two from each side of 6), are shed from each wing. In the fourth calendar-year, at the age of three, the final five primaries, 3, 2, 1, 9 and 10 are dropped. New feathers grow and moult is complete.

Secondary moult

The moult of the fourteen secondary wing feathers in Barn Owls is even more complex. As with primary moult, this commonly begins between May and October in the second calendar-year and takes place over much the same period. In females moult of both the secondary and the tail feathers often begins during incubation, a little before the primaries are shed, while in males it commences later. It usually occurs in two places at once, beginning at number 12 and number 2 or 5, with one or more feathers then being shed next to these. The remaining secondaries are then lost, like the primaries, over a two-year period, inwardly and outwardly from these two centres. Commonly six to eight feathers are shed in the third calendar-year and in the fourth calendar-year, it is usually numbers 1, 4 and 8 that are the last to be replaced to complete the secondary moult.

Tail moult

The full replacement of the twelve tail feathers (rectrices) again usually takes place over a period of two years. The extreme outer two feathers from each side of the tail, followed by the two central feathers, are usually the first to be shed in the second calendar-year. With females, this seems to begin soon after the initial primary has been dropped. With male birds, the rectrices seem to be shed well before any of the wing feathers, judging by the collections I have made at male roosts (where the tail feathers are often the first to be found). The remaining rectrices are then shed in the owls' third and fourth calendar-year, at about the same time as the last of the primary and secondary wing feathers are being dropped.

Subsequent moults

After the moult has been completed, usually when the bird is three years of age, the sequence begins again, with new feathers being replaced more irregularly over a two-to-three-year period. In the wild, however, only a quarter of juvenile Barn Owls ever reach adulthood and those that do have an average life expectancy of only three years, which means that only a relatively small number ever survive to complete their second moult.

Pigmentation is slowly lost from the plumage over successive moults, and this becomes particularly noticeable on the feather bars to the extent that both the wing and tail feathers can sometimes appear almost pure white on older birds. This can be particularly pronounced on captive Barn Owls, which, because they have outlived many of their wild counterparts, commonly reaching the age of twenty or more have therefore gone through perhaps five full moults.

Nestlings: the first and second down

The initial period from hatching to about the twenty-fifth day of life also involves a rapid sequence of feather development involving the growth and shedding of two different types of down and the emergence of the true primary feathers. After hatching, the first short grey down, which is called the protoptile plumage, rapidly grows to cover the upperparts. By the twelfth to fourteenth day a second, more dense, creamy-white down, the mesoptile plumage, begins to appear which is fully grown by the fifteenth to eighteenth day. At this time the facial-disc feathers begin to develop and the primary quills can be seen emerging with the tufts of down at their tips. These begin unfurling at about the twenty-fifth day, and the body feathers begin to grow rapidly. By the thirty-fifth day the primaries have entirely unfurled, and three days later the tail feathers have also appeared. The juveniles' second down is usually completely replaced by the adult plumage between 54 and 60 days of age, when the young are taking their initial flights and at which stage they become indistinguishable from their parents.

11

MOVEMENTS

Once they have chosen their nesting site and foraging grounds Barn Owls are very faithful to these, remaining at the same place in spite of changes and sometimes complete destruction of their habitat. Their reluctance to move seems remarkable, especially when alternative unoccupied foraging areas and nesting sites are often available close by. This means that the bird's initial choice of breeding site determines its breeding success not only in the first year but over its lifetime.

Because most Barn Owls are ringed as juveniles in the nest, it is possible when birds are subsequently found, to determine how far and in which direction they have dispersed from their natal sites. This averages about 9 km. For those ringed as breeding adults and later recovered dead, the average is 4 km, and even this may be high because birds found alive within 5 km of where they were ringed are not recorded. These are average figures and many first-year birds move far greater distances and this is more common in regions of low abundance. Perhaps this is because in these areas where suitable habitat is at a premium and highly fragmented, birds need to move further in order to find new areas. The average dispersal distances for Barn Owls between 1940 and 1988, however, show no real evidence for any increase. Ringing records also confirm that Barn Owls disperse randomly as youngsters and do not favour a particular direction unless restricted by topography. They avoid crossing mountainous or hilly areas or large expanses of sea, although, unlike the Tawny Owl, if pressed they are capable of doing so, as records of continental Barn Owls (*T.a. guttata*) turning up in eastern England and the Channel Islands demonstrate. In the late winter of 1990, for example, I received notification of a bird found in north Lincolnshire which had been ringed in Holland as a nestling, having lived 234 days and travelled 439 km. This was the first such recovery, so the number of these arriving in Britain is likely to be very low. In Guernsey, five unringed dark-breasted birds have also been recorded over the last thirty years.

I am convinced that in Britain young Barn Owls follow river courses when they leave their natal areas, encouraged by the opportunities the prey-rich grassy river banks offer. There is a high incidence of breeding sites on river corridors in Britain, and in many counties the breeding population is strung out almost exclusively along these. In areas where dispersal is restricted by the sea, hills or urban areas, Barn Owls end up in a place which suggests that they followed the only main river away from their nest sites. One colleague has found that of the Barn Owls he has ringed south of Bristol all recoveries have turned up north of Warminster – a direct route along the River Avon.

12

LIFESPAN AND LONGEVITY

How long a Barn Owl lives is perhaps one of the most frequent questions I am asked. These are in fact very short-lived birds, particularly for a bird of prey, having a lifespan of less than a year if we group together both juveniles and adults together and average them out. If we include only those a year or more old and which have therefore already gained some experience in avoiding disaster, the average life expectancy is about three years, even though the oldest ringed Barn Owl reported was 21 years and six month of age! Perhaps a more pertinent question should be how many of the young that are reared in any one year survive to adulthood and breed?

As a rough guide, about 15,000 young Barn Owls are produced annually from about 5000 breeding pairs in Britain and Ireland, with the population at the present time believed to be stable or possibly declining. Assuming a stable population, then on average a total of 15,000 Barn Owls, including both juveniles and adults, must die each year to maintain the status quo, an annual mortality which is sometimes very hard to imagine. In order to offset these losses, the Barn Owl has a phenomenal reproductive capability which under good conditions enables it to keep pace with this heavy rate of mortality.

If we assume that in Britain a single brood of three fledged young is the norm, by the end of the first breeding season there would be five Barn Owls where originally there was only one pair. If all of these and their progeny were to survive and breed over a period of five years, then over 600 Barn Owls would have been produced from the initial pair. On this reckoning, assuming an estimated 5000 breeding pairs in Britain, there would be in excess of three million Barn Owls at the end of this fifth year. Naturally this does not happen. Indeed, the breeding population has in fact declined dramatically over the last fifty years, which shows that the number of young birds being produced has not been able to keep pace with mortality.

Overproduction of young in the breeding season results in competition between individuals for limited food resources. This means that only the fittest, that is those with traits best suited to their particular environment, manage to survive into adulthood to breed. This overproduction, which, as we have seen, is about 15,000 Barn Owls every year, allows populations to recover quickly after a natural catastrophy such as a particularly severe winter, which may have depressed breeding or led to above-average mortality. On the face of it, it is often hard to understand why the intense persecution by man in the 1800s or the devestating effects of organochlorine insecticides in the mid-1900s did not result in the extermination of a species like the Barn Owl. Once the level of overproduction of young birds is taken into account, however, it is not so difficult to understand why populations have such long-term resilience to these forms of man-made disaster, although eventual recovery also depends on the surviving birds having safe and preferably well-dispersed havens during the difficult years.

It is of interest, and important for conservation reasons, to try to understand within which section of the population mortality is occurring most and how and where these birds are dying. The ringing scheme of the British Trust for Ornithology can provide important information about the survival rates, dispersal and causes of death among wild Barn Owls. Since 1909, 13,000 Barn Owls have been ringed in the UK and 1500 have been recovered. Although the proportion of ringed birds found dead is less than 15 per cent, the sample size is large enough to provide answers to many questions. The above figures relating to average lifespan of juvenile and adult Barn Owls have been derived from such data.

As we have seen, the levels of winter mortality are likely to be higher for those Barn Owls living at altitudes greater than 150 m and those in the colder regions of eastern England than for birds occupying lower ground or places in western Britain, where the winter climate is much milder. When we look at the average survival rate of Barn Owls in Britain, although this varies in different regions, we find that it is only 18–29 per cent for juveniles (those birds in their first year), while for the more experienced adults (between one and two years of age) survival is 55–70 per cent, the lower figures referring to birds occupying more marginal habitats on higher ground. Interestingly, these figures are similar to those reported for Barn Owls in eastern Germany and Switzerland. For each successful new breeding pair, therefore, about 1.25 individuals would be present in the second year, leaving room in a stable population for 0.75 juveniles. Since on average three young owls fledge annually from every nest in the UK and only 18–29 per cent of these ever achieve adulthood and breed, this does in fact suggest that 0.75 juveniles per pair are on hand to maintain the population at a constant level. I have, of course, described this rather simplistically, and although in reality things are not quite so straightforward it does serve to illustrate how figures such as these can be used to understand more about the reasons for population change.

On the whole, populations are governed by the amount of available food, particularly during the winter, and when this is provided by man (either directly or indirectly) breeding numbers can be maintained at artificially high levels; conversely when this is withdrawn, populations will quite naturally crash. As I have said before, probably the main cause of the Barn Owl's decline in Britain, and also in the rest of Europe, was the sudden loss from the farming scene of the prey-rich rickyard, which would until the 1940s have provided this owl with a dependable artificial food source. Today, most mortality still occurs, perhaps not surprisingly during the winter. With juvenile Barn Owls this is due mainly to starvation resulting from their inexperience in hunting in unfavourable weather, together with the general reduction in the availability of food at this time.

13

MORTALITY AND CAUSES OF DECLINE

One inherent problem with collecting records of dead birds from the general public, which is what the BTO's ringing scheme largely relies upon, is that the reported causes of death can be biased in favour of those most easily identified by the public, usually during their daily activities while travelling. In my study of Barn Owl mortality, from 1982–86, I tried to avoid some of the possible bias by encouraging input from a wider cross-section of the public. I requested information from farmers, landowners and other country people who would have an equal chance of finding a dead Barn Owl on their farm as they would on a road.

In the event, 746 records from Britain and fifty records from Ireland were used to investigate the causes of mortality in Britain, these data originating from landworkers (40 per cent) and from the general public (60 per cent), the latter including birdwatchers and ornithologists. Taxidermists were also approached for records through the Taxidermists' Guild and these, together with those kindly supplied by the Institute of Terrestrial Ecology, allowed me to achieve more specific information about the mortality patterns and the causes of death of male and female Barn Owls.

Even though the information originated from a wide cross-section of individuals, by far the most significant single cause of death was road accidents, accounting for 52 per cent of all mortality in Britain (49 per cent in Ireland). In the UK as a whole, the contribution of road mortality to the annual death rate of Barn Owls has risen, according to figures from the BTO from 14–27 per cent between 1944 and 1964; 33–34 per cent between 1965 and 1970, 40–41 per cent during the period 1971–76; 38–40 per cent between 1977 and 1982 and 48–49 per cent during 1983–85 (Percival 1990). The first figure in each set gives the percentage contribution for adults and the second that for juveniles, and with the possible exception of the early period these figures indicate that juveniles are no more susceptible to being hit by vehicles than are adults. The increase in the extent of road-traffic mortality over the last twenty years or so could have been anticipated for a number of reasons. Both the speed and the numbers of vehicles have increased considerably over this period. Major new roads have been developed which have cut through otherwise prime habitat, and the increasing extent of unmanaged roadside verges offers tempting feeding places as the amount of rough grassland has declined on farmland from unprecedented levels in the 1930s to a mere remnant today.

With their low-level hunting, Barn Owls inevitably fall victim. High-sided lorries present a particular problem to owls flying along verges, because they become sucked into the slipstream almost as easily as a sheet of tissue paper and are often killed or injured by a following vehicle. Collision also occurs, again most often with high lorries, as Barn Owls are flying across roads, usually where there is a low gate or gap in the hedge. John Cooper, a friend and well-known raptor vet who kindly conducted postmortem investigations for my Barn Owl survey, was able to show that the majority of road casualties suffered fractures to the right wing, indicating that most collisions are the result of owls emerging suddenly into the path of traffic from the nearside verge and that those emerging from the offside verge were usually able to rise above the traffic. Barn Owls are not only killed while hunting but are also killed while apparently sitting motionless in the road. Having witnessed this myself, I believe that these birds were undoubtedly 'still-hunting' using the clear open road to catch small mammals moving across the tarmac, a type of 'sit-and-wait' technique that is not uncommon on farm and forest tracks in Africa and Malaysia.

No study is complete, and no true assessment can be made of the factors influencing population levels, without a firm understanding of the major causes of mortality. Although it is possible to study and analyse both the type and the extent of each of these causes, it is more difficult to interpret their individual importance in relation to a species' long-term decline. Collision with traffic, for example, can cause heavy annual mortality, yet we could reasonably conclude that, even in the absence of road deaths, many of these birds would have died before attaining breeding age, entirely as a result of natural pressures. Also, while collision may have been the ultimate outcome, the stress caused by hunger may have been the primary factor encouraging the birds to exploit these hazardous roadside hunting grounds.

It has been suggested by some researchers that because road-traffic victims appear to be below average weight they were destined to die anyway through natural causes. If we examine this in more detail, however, we find that these casualties cover a full range of weights from 220 g to 390 g. Although the average of 290 g is towards the lower end of this scale, this is not unexpected since most of these birds would have been in the process of foraging at the time, putting them in a position of maximum risk over their well-fed counterparts. In other words, this sample of the population is always going to favour lower-weight birds, not because they are inferior but because they simply had not eaten. Three voles for example weigh about 60 g, so, if the same owl had been weighed after such a meal it would effectively have been 60 g heavier, but once back in the security of its roost would be at little risk of death. In addition, specimens often suffer some dehydration before they are found and weighed. The weights of road casualties could therefore be expected in all probability to be 40 g or so less than the 340 g reported for live owls in winter (when the majority of road casualties are found). These live owls would in most instances have been weighed at the roost with either a full or partially full gut and before they had ejected their pellet (which they do as they are about to leave the site). It is likely, therefore, that the lower weights recorded for road victims are simply a reflection of these factors, and that Barn Owls killed in this way are in fact likely to represent a true cross-section of the live population and are not simply substandard birds which were destined not to reach breeding age. A study by Geoff Pearce in Devon using coloured rings has shown that first-year road casualties subsequently rehabilitated from injury, and released back into the wild successfully, are now into their third breeding season, having produced young every year. Certainly there was no suggestion here of inferiority, and it is generally the rule that most of the poor quality that is found in birds is not genetic but is due to environmental factors such as inadequate quantity of food or bad weather.

Whatever the live condition of Barn Owls killed on Britain's roads, it is still not possible to know what proportion would have succumbed to natural causes before they had the chance to breed and whether therefore the levels of road-traffic mortality are now a significant contributory cause of the Barn Owl's overall decline in the UK. Nevertheless, it would appear that when major roads are constructed through traditional Barn Owl habitat they can have a devastating effect on local populations by fragmenting habitats together with their associated ditches and hedgerows, resulting in the exposure of these birds to the hazards of fast-moving vehicles. My findings strongly suggest that, soon after major road schemes are completed in areas where Barn Owls are present, mortality increases, with the result that local populations are rapidly depleted and within a few years the area within about 2 km of the new road no longer supports breeding Barn Owls. More recent data, gathered on one of the newest motorways, the M5 in Avon, showed that in the first year 48 casualties had been found, but by the sixth year only a handful were being reported. The apparent decline in numbers seems to be supported from a recent survey, which has confirmed that Barn Owls were no longer breeding in Avon. A point may therefore be arrived at when the mortality caused by a man-induced pressure reaches such high proportions that this pressure becomes a significant factor limiting a species' numbers and, as such, is partially or wholly responsible for a population decline. Human persecution, which led to the widespread decline of birds of prey in the nineteenth century, is one example of the way in which a single, unrelenting human activity can exact a heavy long-term toll on population levels.

The next most important category I have termed 'no apparent cause', which accounts for 23 per cent of deaths, and refers to birds showing no sign of injury, found where there was no visible hazard – mainly to those specimens lying in a field or an open farm building, for example. While this group may include a few birds which had previously flown into some object, and those which had succumbed to chemical poisoning, the large majority refer to Barn Owls which have died of starvation or some natural cause. Interestingly, many in this class were found waterlogged following periods of rain. Since large numbers of casualties are found between September and November, it is likely that the majority represent young birds which have become stranded and chilled while learning to hunt; as I have stressed before, this seems to be a serious natural hazard in Britain and one which I believe has not previously been fully appreciated.

Drowning constitutes the second-highest known cause of mortality of Barn Owls, accounting for 6 per cent of all deaths. This occurs in water butts, cattle troughs, tanks and slurry pits, and also in ponds, lakes, rivers and even the sea. Of the drowning reports I received, 60 per cent occurred in July and all involved females, this being the only time during the year when any seasonal difference in mortality between the sexes is observed. The beginning of July coincides with the month during the breeding cycle when most females begin to emerge from the soiled confines of the nest site, having incubated and brooded continuously throughout an eight-week period. It seems probable, therefore, that drowning occurs as a result of unsuccessful bathing attempts to remove soiling and parasites after the prolonged nest confinement. Supportive evidence for this arises from studies with captive Barn Owls, where it has been recognized that after brooding has been completed the females leave the nestbox and immediately bathe, while at other times of the year, bathing is more unusual (Bunn et al. 1982).

Flying into overhead wires and fence wires represents 5 per cent of mortalities. Perhaps one of the earliest fatalities to a Barn Owl from tele-graph wires was reported by Stevenson and Southwell in Norfolk in 1866. Today, some fatalities may occur through electrocution as a result of earthing on overhead power cables, especially those serving the electric rail network (where a disproportionate number of small-raptor casualties are reported). Fence wires are also a hazard to Barn Owls on farmland, although numerically many more such casualties were recorded among Tawny Owls, probably a consequence of their larger numbers rather than increased susceptibility. Most of the Barn Owl deaths in this category involved barbed wire, and carcases were usually found hanging by the feet, no doubt because of the bird's practice of dangling its legs in flight. Other reports concerned birds caught in fruit netting, chicken wire and tennis nets.

Barn Owls often become trapped within buildings, having fallen down the chimneys of houses left temporarily unoccupied. They are also found having been inadvertently shut inside barns and warehouses or trapped within the roof space or ducting of commercial buildings. This is responsible for about 3 per cent of deaths. It seems that the Barn Owl, in its quest to find dark and secluded quarters in which to roost and nest suffers more from this cause of death than do other species of owl.

Inevitably, persecution is the cause least likely to be reported and has, therefore, been much underrepresented in studies of mortality, especially concerning birds of prey, many of which are legally protected by special penalties. Nevertheless, for Barn Owls, the noticeable downward trend in persecution, from 12 per cent of total reported mortality during the period 1910–54, to 5 per cent between 1955 and 1969 (Glue 1971) and just 3 per cent today, is an encouraging one.

Two classes of pesticide were implicated in my mortality study, causing 3 per cent of total mortality in England, Wales and Scotland, although in Ireland it was over 20 per cent. Rodenticides accounted for 88 per cent of reported poisonings, and molluscicides (slug and snail poison) the remainder. Most reported incidents correspond with those regions where the potent 'second-generation' anticoagulants (difenacoum, bromadiolone and brodi-facoum) are commonly used, particularly in central-southern England. Owl corpses were usually found eight to 25 days after baiting commenced. A number of incidents involved two or more birds, usually found during the winter season between November and March. Slug and snail poisons (metaldehyde) accounted for two separate incidents. Reports were confined to oilseed-rape fields in south-eastern England, in situations where large quantities of pellets had been applied. Barn Owl carcases were found close to the fields and were accompanied in two instances by numbers of shrew corpses around the edges of the treated area.

Collision with moving trains has been a relatively common unnatural cause of mortality to the Barn Owl, although today it represents only 2 per cent of deaths. Perhaps the earliest record involved a collision with the funnel of a steam locomotive travelling between Kelso and Roxburgh in Scotland in 1876, and not long after this the importance of railside foraging grounds to owls became recognized. Between 1910 and 1969, Glue found that train victims accounted for 11 per cent of reported mortality. In spite of the increased speed of modern diesel and electric units today, the loss of over 11,000 km (7000 miles) of the rail network in the mid-1960s may in part account for the apparent reduction in the numbers of Barn Owls dying from this cause. Four instances of aircraft strikes were also reported at a military and commercial airfields.

Seasonal mortality

Seasonal mortality shows a fascinating pattern. The death rate is lowest in the period leading up to May and throughout the following month of June, when most females are safely confined to the nest site. A noticeable July peak then follows. This involves mainly females coinciding with the time when they leave the nest site for the first time since egg-laying began. A large proportion of these July deaths is the result of drowning, probably, as I have already mentioned, the result of the hen's attempts to clean up after her long period of nest confinement. The average fledging date is in mid-August. Thereafter, a steep increase in mortality begins in September, reaching a peak during October and November at the time when most young birds are attaining independence. Roadside hunting may increase in response to seasonal food shortage at this time. Although male mortality appears to lag slightly behind that of females, the pattern shows no major differences between the sexes over these months. By December mortality falls, only to rise once again to a large peak during the months of February and March, when snow cover is more prolonged and the stress brought on by lack of food is greatest. Unlike the previous October and November peak, which includes about 65 per cent juveniles, this late-winter peak involves older birds, with juveniles now accounting for only 40 per cent of the total (Glue 1973). While no significant differences occur between the sexes during February to March, there appears to be a somewhat increased trend towards males becoming victims. This is possibly the result of the additional stresses involved in locating and defending good hunting grounds in readiness for courtship and breeding. Finally, the ratio of male to female mortality, sampled from the population during my four-year study, is approximately equal, at 82 male and 73 female Barn Owls.

Barn Owls have long, broad wings making them adapted to slow, low-level flight

Predators and competitors

Today Barn Owls have few natural enemies, but persecution by man in the nineteenth century led to much slaughter. This was largely in the name of game preservation, which began in about 1825. Once the breech-loading gun had been introduced in 1832, persecution of all birds of prey began in earnest, and it was not long before landlords were offering bounty payments to gamekeepers, the value of which was based upon the number and type of birds of prey successfully shot or trapped each year. Attitudes began to change towards the end of the century, as keepers realized that Barn Owls were interested only in small rodents which were eating their corn. Taxidermy and millinery, however, continued to flourish, stimulated by Victorian fashion and the passion for collecting wildlife specimens of all types. The ringing records indicate that the number of Barn Owls increased dramatically, albeit temporarily, during both World Wars, when keepers were otherwise engaged. As the twentieth century has progressed, persecution by man no longer remains the serious threat it had once been.

Barn Owls, like other birds of prey which are out in daylight, are commonly mobbed by other birds, but these are not predators in the true sense and are usually shrugged off or simply tolerated. Unlike the Tawny Owl Barn Owls do not seem to attract so much attention from smaller birds.

The Goshawk, however, is perhaps a more common avian predator of Barn Owls than we think, and in Europe it has previously been identified as such (Mikkola 1976). In spite of its low numbers, it is widely distributed in Britain and is perhaps the Barn Owl's greatest natural enemy. These large raptors, renowned for their relentless pursuit of owls, have little difficulty in

Fig. 8 *Mortality all causes by month (1982–6)*

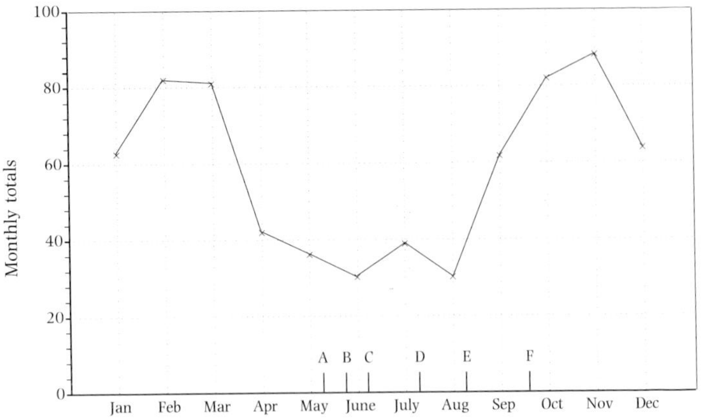

Notes: A – mean mid egg laying time; B – incubation and beginning of moult; C – mean mid hatch;
D – continuous brooding ceases; E – mean fledging time; F – young become independent

capturing them if they are out during daylight, and during my survey four records were received of Goshawks taking Barn Owls. Buzzards have accounted for a further three incidents since the study ended and a female Sparrowhawk for another. Peregrines have also been seen to kill Barn Owls when the opportunity arises, but this is probably quite an unusual occurrence since these two species are only rarely found together. A Fulmar was responsible for an incident on sea cliffs in Yorkshire, death arising as a result of being sprayed with Fulmar oil. Mink, Stoats, Weasels and Brown Rats were also implicated in my studies on mortality, and in all cases these involved incubating or brooding Barn Owls nesting in vulnerable situations, usually low down or on the ground in hollow stumps and in fallen trees. More recently, reports have emerged of Pine Martens occupying nestboxes in Scotland, with two instances of possible predation. Surprisingly, predation by domestic cats appears to be very rare despite their presence on farmland, but I can imagine that when the two confront each other their similar threat display and vocal hissing must be quite an experience. In all, predation represented just over 2 per cent of all deaths in my study and is probably quite insignificant in overall terms.

Today, the highly adaptable Tawny Owl not only is present in municipal parks, copses and woodland throughout mainland Britain but can also be found on more open farmland wherever there is a small stand of trees. Its current British population is in the range of 10,000–100,000 pairs and its numbers are undoubtedly towards the upper limit of this range, suggesting that it is now probably about fifteen to twenty times more common than the Barn Owl. It is tempting to conclude that its probable increase this century has had something to do with the introduction of the Grey Squirrel and the many suitable dreys the latter is able to provide as nesting sites for this owl. It seems unlikely, however, that this is a serious competitor of the

Barn Owl, since it generally feeds on a much wider range of prey and only rarely nests in buildings, although in eastern England, where Barn Owls mainly use tree cavities, there is more competition. The Tawny Owl selects its territory and breeding site earlier than other tree-nesting species, and may on some occasions prevent Barn Owls reoccupying their traditional nest sites which they may have vacated during the winter.

Tawny Owls can kill Barn Owls which are competing for nesting sites (Mikkola 1976), and a few reports to the survey involved Barn Owls at tree sites. Two other reports concerned Tawny Owls aggressively dislodging Barn Owls and occupying their sites. Potential competition between these two species for nesting sites and also food is, however, likely to be significant only in areas where the Short-tailed Vole provides the main source of food, such as in the commercial forests of Scotland and Wales where both owls can be found hunting and nesting in close proximity around the woodland edge.

Although not true predators, Jackdaws are undoubtedly the Barn Owl's worst enemy, because they compete tenaciously for cavities. During my survey I constantly came across records where Barn Owls had disappeared after Jackdaws had taken over their nesting cavity, usually in an old tree. Because these were largely subjective I tended to ignore them when considering reasons for the Barn Owl's decline, but more recent events which have affected my own field work have given me cause to think again.

When we began putting up nestboxes on poles in Lincolnshire, there was an immediate take-up by Barn Owls, indicating that the previous lack of nest sites had been limiting the population in this region, so more pole boxes were erected. Immediately, Jackdaws began moving into these two-tier boxes, and by the third year, 28 of the 46 boxes (each two-chambered) were held by Jackdaws. At one site, Barn Owls which had managed to occupy the box early were able to hold their own and removed the young Jackdaw chicks from the upper chamber dropping them on the ground. On the whole, I am left wondering if in the absence of Jackdaws more Barn Owls would have nested in the boxes. Throughout much of East Anglia, where Barn Owls no longer occupy their traditional tree nest Jackdaws are in residence. Whether or not they have excluded the Barn Owls by filling the chamber entrance with nest material or were occupying a site from which the owls had already disappeared is difficult to tell, but I am sure they are significant competitors in many areas where natural nest sites are limited. The tenacity of Jackdaws has also been shown in Wiltshire, where two pairs of Tawny Owls had become completely entombed by these birds which had built their stick nest on top of the incubating owls (Lewis 1992). As I write, a pair of Jackdaws has filled the landing ledge and entrance of a tree box where a Barn Owl is currently incubating six eggs! It seems that the owls do little to ward off the Jackdaws, but the speed at which these birds can deposit sticks probably gives them little opportunity. A colleague has shown also that Magpies, too, are potential aggressors, having witnessed a pack attempting to remove owlets from a nestbox in an open hay barn, even though the female Barn Owl was in attendance. Had they been allowed to continue, they probably would have succeeded.

Winter food and climate

Climate is the ultimate factor governing the type of vegetation that will grow in an area, which in turn largely dictates the type and range of annual communities that can be supported. Clearly, there are vast differences between habitats found at the equator and those at the poles but even over relatively short distances, major differences can be found. Climate strongly influences the type of crops which can be grown and the timing and mechanism of harvesting, so that, for example, hay-making is favoured in the dry eastern regions of Britain and silage in the west.

When long-term changes in climate occur, they can often be identified by changes in the fauna and flora. In Britain, following the cold snowy winters which occurred between 1860 and 1899, fifteen of which were severe, the new century began with a remarkable overall warming of the climate leading to forty years of mild winters, only one of which was severe. Between 1900 and 1940 this warming became so great that it could no longer be overlooked or denied. It led to a general easing up on such practices as laying in food stocks for periods of winter snow in isolated habitations and allowed exotic fruits such as apricots, peaches and grapes to be grown for the first time in many areas (Lamb 1965, 1970).

In Britain the Barn Owl is on the extreme fringes of its world breeding range and as such becomes highly sensitive to even small changes in climate, particularly when these involve an increase in winter severity, to which it is poorly adapted. As we have seen, severe winters, particularly those involving above-average snow cover, can influence the bird's breeding productivity and survival. When these climatic changes become part of a sustained worsening pattern, then numbers can show a long-term downward trend and in situations where an already fragile population exists can lead to extinction. However, the actions of man, who has attempted since his arrival on this planet to mould the environment to suit his immediate needs, can sometimes unintentionally cushion otherwise vulnerable animals against the climatic effects of nature.

The Barn Owl has undoubtedly benefited from the the activities of man following the clearance of forests and the provision of barns which enabled it to nest. Perhaps the single most important item that farmers inadvertently provided, and which lies at the heart of the Barn Owl's success in surviving and increasing in northern Europe, was the ricks of harvested corn which for hundreds of years became an expanding feature of the stackyard and barn of almost every farmstead. These, together with the cattleyards and straw-bedded stables used to house large number of working horses, literally spilled grain and other food into the mouths of hungry rodents, including the Brown Rat which appeared on British shores in about 1730. The old farmyard therefore offered the Barn Owl shelter and plentiful prey in winter and early spring, enabling it to survive and to expand its numbers when it would otherwise have been highly vulnerable to starvation.

By the 1940s all this was about to change. In 1942 the combine harvester had been introduced into Britain, so the storage of corn in

The pole trap was outlawed in the late nineteenth century. Thankfully, this form of persecution is now uncommon.

sheaves stacked in unthreshed ricks was no longer necessary and almost overnight the rickyard disappeared from the farming scene, substituted by close-cut fields of stubble, with grain protected within silos and rodent-proof bins. This new form of mechanization and the increasing use of the tractor meant that the working horse and its stores of winter fodder and bedding also disappeared, making the farmyard a far less attractive place for the small rodents and the predators which once feasted on them.

From the early 1940s the winter climate worsened, a trend which continued until the early 1980s. During the mild period between 1900 and 1939, the annual snow cover, taken from a sample of low-lying meteorological stations in Britain, averaged just twelve days, and only in 1917 did it exceed twenty days. From 1940 to 1986 average annual snow cover rose to 21 days, and in 22 of these years, snow lay on the ground for twenty or more days; indeed, the level exceeded thirty days in nine of these winters, and in the most severe ones of 1947, 1963 and 1979 it exceeded forty days.

For the first time in farming history the Barn Owl was being deprived of its dependable winter food supply, just when the worsening winter weather made this even more vital. The population needed to readjust and stabilize at a lower level because of the sudden reduction in the winter carrying capacity of its environment.

Barn Owl numbers in England and Wales were estimated at 12,000 pairs by George Blaker in 1932. Numbers were highest in the cereal-growing south-east and central regions, according to the county reports published between 1880 and 1919 which was confirmed later by George Blaker's Census in 1932.

Since 1932, the greatest declines have been in Essex, west Suffolk and west Norfolk, Leicestershire, west Lincolnshire, Northamptonshire, Cambridgeshire, Huntingdonshire, Hertfordshire and Bedfordshire which are the snowiest and coldest areas in lowland Britain (annual snow cover is rarely less than fifteen days' duration and January temperatures average 3 °C or below). With the disappearance of the stackyard from these cereal-dominated areas, it comes as little surprise to find that these are also the places where Barn Owl numbers have suffered most over the last sixty years, to the extent that today they hold the lowest Barn Owl densities anywhere in Britain.

Blaker in 1932 showed that the Barn Owl was equally abundant on land up to 400 m above sea level; indeed he identified a high population density in the northern lakelands of Cumbria where an abnormal increase appeared to be occurring at the time of the census, while others had found similar increases in numbers in central and southern Scotland somewhat earlier. These changes may well have been stimulated by the increasing area of young conifer plantations coupled with the mild winters of this period. Since then, after almost fifty years of increased and sustained winter severity, the preferred habitat of the Barn Owl has changed so that today it is rarely found above 150 m except in the south-west where it can more commonly reach 200 m. In addition to central and south-east of England, where it has all but disappeared, it has also been lost from all but the coastal districts of Wales and even from the downlands of southern England, which includes the hills of the Cotswolds, the Chilterns to the Northamptonshire uplands and extending into Leicestershire, the north Lincolnshire Wolds and the south Staffordshire plateau. Altitude is one of the main criteria for determining the number of days over which snow lies, for not only is snowfall itself heavier on higher ground but temperatures fall with increasing altitude at a rate of about 1 °C for every 150 m.

It is perhaps not surprising therefore that populations at these higher altitudes were the most noticeably affected by the worsening winter climate. Snow cover increases by about nine days for every 150-m rise in elevation in lower latitudes and by about 24 days in the higher latitudes of the Central Highlands of Scotland. Almost three-quarters of land in Britain and Ireland is above 150 m and during 1941–70 most of this received an average of fifteen to twenty days' annual snow cover, so that in a large proportion of Britain the Barn Owl is now a rare breeding bird. Topography therefore limits the Barn Owl's range and thus its numbers in the British Isles today, but, should the milder winters of the 1990s continue, these more marginal lands may once again be colonized in places where rough grassland and nesting sites are also freely available.

Loss of summer feeding habitat

Nowhere has the drive to maximize production and efficiency in agriculture, which has been aided by advances in mechanization, been more dramatic than in Britain where since World War II about 40 per cent of freehold rough grazing in lowland England has been lost together with 95 per cent of hay meadows. Today, fields are often temporarily sown with a single species of rye grass. The management of these meadows used to involve a single cut of hay, but now these short-rotation grasslands with their repeated cuts for silage no longer allow vole and shrew populations to build up; indeed these small mammals simply do not exist in any number in these intensively managed green deserts. As a result, the Barn Owl has become increasingly dependent on rough-grassland field margins along hedgerow and woodland edge, but these, too, have been lost: an estimated 225,000 km (140,000 miles) of hedgerow disappeared between 1946 and 1974, as well as 35–50 per cent of mature woodland since 1933. This again has been encouraged by the drive towards more efficient single-enterprise farms and increased urbanization.

The loss of these important foraging habitats has been greater in the cereal-growing regions of East Anglia, the Midlands, south-eastern England, and in Cumbria, Lancashire, Cheshire, Staffordshire, Dorset and Avon, where there have been major increases in the stocking density of sheep and cattle. The disappearance of whole meadows and grassland edge has therefore been greatest in those regions of single-enterprise farming, where crops now dominate 75–95 per cent of agricultural land and where stocking densities are the highest in Britain at 50–70 livestock units per 40 ha (100 acres) of farmland (livestock units represent the sum of all classes of livestock weighted according to their grassland food requirement).

In most of the cereal regions of East Anglia, East Midlands and the south-east, linear grasslands, with the exception of roadside edge, have been lost entirely on farmland as modern harvesting machines have demanded larger fields in which to operate and the loss of stock has obviated the need for enclosures in the form of hedgerow or ditch. In 1947, for example, the length of hedgerow per square kilometre of non-urban land in the major cereal-growing areas was 6.9 km; today it has declined to 5.3 km, a loss of 23 per cent and much of that which remains is now a series of closely pruned stumps. The width of rough grassland along hedgerows has been reduced to a remnant of what it was, since it is now farmed to the very base as every inch of the field is utilized for cropping. All of this has reduced the once expansive field margins which were used to turn the working horse and carry away the harvested crops. Collectively, these would have provided substantial amounts of grassland on farms and attracted small mammals in large numbers. It is doubtful that Field Voles or shrews are able to inhabit these narrow strips of grass along hedgerows today, and the few Wood Mice and Bank Voles which be present in these slender margins are unlikely to be found in sufficient numbers to attract Barn Owls.

The overall result is that in the cereal prairies, the only places which are not under tillage are the coastal marshes and the banks of rivers and ditches, where crop production cannot easily be increased without expensive drainage operations. The specialized cattle- and sheep-rearing areas of western Britain fare little better. In the lowlands of Cumbria, Lancashire, Wales and many of the counties of south-western England, the increase in stocking rates, particularly of sheep, means that the close-cropped grasslands here are little better than bowling greens and no longer attract small mammals. Because sheep are both at very high density and particularly agile, even the margins of these fields usually provided by a ditch, river bank or hedgerow are grazed tightly right up to their very edges. In other areas, such as the counties of Cheshire and Staffordshire, wire fences (which have increased by 30 per cent at the expense of hedges since 1947) fail to offer any grassy base. High stocking density also leads to trampling of the grass sward, eventually destroying the tussock structure which is so important to maintain good vole and shrew populations.

Modern husbandry, too, has contributed to the decline in small-mammal prey for the Barn Owl. Cattle sheds are now commonly concreted or slatted with wood to aid cleaning, and carefully optimized feeding methods provide little spillage or waste. As a consequence, commensal rodents are not so attracted to farmyards as they once were.

At the end of my survey, the southern and south-western regions of England, Wales and Scotland were faring well in terms of Barn Owl numbers. It was likely that the more traditional nature of farming here provided more in the way of good stock-proof hedges and banks with their grassy margins, and the much smaller fields allowed for more controlled grazing. Average farmholdings were 8–120 ha (20–300 acres) in size, compared with those in eastern and central-southern regions which were more commonly 200–400 ha (500–1000 acres). The less specialized nature of farming also meant that only 25–50 per cent of land was under tillage, and more extensive woodlands provided a greater extent of prey-rich field margins. In 1947 the length of linear features on farmland in the south-west region was 12.6 km per square kilometre; in 1985 this appeared to have changed very little, to 11.3 km, a loss of only 10 per cent. However, there are now worrying signs that Barn Owl numbers are dwindling, particularly in the county of Avon, where until major conservation effort was implemented by the Hawk and Owl Trust in 1991, no successful breeding had been proved since 1988. The Somerset Levels at the time of the survey were considered one of the most important strongholds in the south-west, but now appear to support far fewer pairs. Wherever one looks to find a reason for this apparently escalating decline in the south-west, habitat destruction through overgrazing by sheep seems to be a recurrent theme. In many other areas horse-riding has become an important pastime, and in the more heavily populated regions of central-southern England a great deal of the remaining grassland is now heavily grazed by large numbers of horses and quickly becomes unsuitable for small mammals. While many impoverished landscapes may in fact be able to support a single Barn Owl needing perhaps six small mammals a day, it is only those prey-rich grasslands which can deliver about twenty to thirty small mammals a day that will be occupied during the breeding season. This is something many people fail to realize when trying to understand why Barn Owls are no longer present in an area or on an individual farm.

Isolation of remaining populations

Migratory or very mobile birds can recover quite quickly and repopulate whole countries following a serious decline. Populations, particularly of sedentary species such as the Barn Owl, can remain self-sustaining, however, only if they are able to exist in sufficiently large numbers to enable them to recover from the heavy mortality inflicted by a severe winter, for example, or if their depleted numbers can be reinforced by new birds moving in from other areas. The total disappearance of Barn Owls from what still appears to be areas of good habitat can often be attributed to the fact that the remnant isolated populations have become separated by wide expanses of hostile land which provides little chance of young birds moving in to reinforce numbers. In other words, what had been lost were the prey-rich dispersal networks which were once provided by the rough-grassland pastures and margins along hedgerow, river and ditch inter-linking larger areas of prime habitat, farm to farm and county. Even those remaining breeding strongholds in Britain are becoming extremely vulnerable because of their decreasing size and the lack of dispersal oppor-tunities, with the result that they may not be with us much longer. A plot of all known breeding records outside the strongholds can be seen as thin strands which follow the main river and stream networks. This suggests that Barn Owls use these natural features for dispersal and that they offer the major means for countrywide continuity for this bird.

The loss of habitat continuity has become an important reason for the Barn Owl's continuing decline, and it is undoubtedly one of the most difficult problems to solve since it requires enormous input to restore, demanding a truly national conservation strategy. This approach is the cornerstone of the Hawk and Owl Trust's conservation policy through its project, The Barn Owl Conservation Network, and its habitat restoratin programme, the Farmland, Riverside and Forestry Link Initiative, which is already achieving some promising signs of recovery in many regions of Britain.

Loss of nest sites

Although the numbers of old trees have declined over the last fifty years, owing to Dutch Elm Disease, storms, hedgerow clearance and overmaturity, and farm buildings because of neglect and conversion into dwellings, there is little evidence to suggest that this is the primary cause of the Barn Owl's decline. These losses have, however, contributed and are becoming an increasingly mportant factor. The most common nest site found in agricultural buildings is on or between hay or straw bales and it can hardly be said that these sites are in short supply because they can still be found on most farms throughout Britain. In the Home Counties, for example, where populations are now exceedingly low and Barn Owls favour tree cavities within isolated parkland or hedgerow trees, many of these sites are still freely available yet only a very small proportion are now occupied. In my own patch of Hertfordshire, where numbers have dropped to just two or three breeding pairs, I was able to locate 28 suitable tree cavities of appropriate size and condition, some of which had been traditional sites for this bird in the past, but not one has been used by Barn Owls during the many years I have been studying this area. In general terms we have lost many suitable hollow trees in Britain over the last two decades from severe storms and Dutch Elm Disease, yet a study I conducted of hollow-tree sites which were located on the path of the 'Great Storm' which occurred in southern England in 1987 showed that only a small number were adversely affected and there was evidence that those owls pairs involved had found alternative sites in the area (Shawyer 1988).

At the end of my survey, in 1985, the total number of nesting boxes available in Britain and Ireland was probably in the order of 6000, yet only 112 boxes were recorded as being used from a total of 2200 breeding sites where a full description of the site was given by the observer. Again, assuming that the majority of these boxes were well sited, this suggests that nesting places were not a major factor limiting the bird's numbers otherwise many more of them would presumably have been used.

The pressures on remaining nesting and roosting sites are increasing, however, to the extent that nest-site loss is now a more serious problem in some areas. Many farm buildings whose openings were designed to permit horse and cart were already redundant by the 1960s because they could no longer accommodate the large tractors and combine harvesters. Today, these neglected buildings are either so derelict that they afford little or no shelter for Barn Owls or have already been pulled down. The more substantial barns were converted to dwellings in the fashionable housing boom of the mid-1980s, and in most cases, little was done to install owl lofts or some other alternative nesting place which could have retained a few pairs where the level of human disturbance was not too great. Of those old farm outbuildings and derelict cottages which remain in good habitat, their dilapidated state and remoteness make them exciting places, especially for children, and as a result they are subject to increasing human disturbance. It is perhaps this disturbance factor more than any other that renders many of these buildings unsuitable for Barn Owls.

When the survey ended one-third of the nesting sites in trees were in Elms (equivalent to about 500 sites in Britain as a whole), even though most were either dead or dying. A large proportion of these nest sites will have now gone as the trees have been felled or have simply fallen over, but this does not necessarily mean that the birds were lost from the area. In the eastern counties of England, where most of these tree-nesting Barn Owls are to be found, there are usually more than enough hollow Oaks, Ash trees (and still Elms in some areas) to provide breeding sites for this bird.

While the loss of nest places is unlikely in itself to be the main cause of the Barn Owl's decline, both the nest site and the habitat together are required if these birds are to be attracted to stay and breed, and this combination is becoming more difficult to find. For example, permanent set-aside, Environmentally Sensitive Areas and other government incentives for the creation of more traditional farming practices have led to recent increases in rough grassland, but suitable nearby nesting sites are frequently lacking simply because they have been removed during the prosperous farming years and, unlike the new grasslands, are not so easily reinstated. What I am therefore saying is that, once habitats are re-created and the main cause of the problem addressed, something else will begin to limit the population from expanding. A new conservation need then becomes paramount, in this case to expand the numbers of nesting and roosting sites by artificial means. This is increasingly likely to be the situation as more and more land is taken out of agricultural production and put over to grassland, and every farm and every region may need to be assessed individually from the conservation viewpoint.

The Hawk and Owl Trust has already shown that in areas where suitable habitat is present or has been restored, the population can be stabilized and increased to the extent that by 1992 over 800 of its nest boxes were used by breeding Barn Owls in the UK. A Trust scheme in south-west Scotland which began in 1982 has now seen an increase in the numbers of nestboxes used annually from just two in the first year to 52 by 1992, with over 800 owlets having fledged from these boxes over this period, simply because, although habitat was available, the area was beginning to lack suitable nesting sites. Without this help, the original population is likely have fallen dramatically as the dilapidated cottages and derelict farm buildings were lost to decay. Today the farmland population has grown to 80 pairs. In 1985, the Forestry Commission expanded the Trust's scheme on afforested lands in the region and began erecting plastic drums at nest sites on conifer trees, mainly around the edges of mature forest. Again, Barn Owls, probably offspring from the farmland sites, began to occupy these drums and, although productivity appeared to be consistently lower than in the farmland boxes, as many as 31 pairs used these forest-edge sites in the peak vole year of 1988. Both projects provided a clear indication that, in this region at least, habitat was not limiting the population but the availability of nest sites was. In Lincolnshire, where suitable nesting and roosting sites were few and far between in this flat fenland region, nestboxes mounted on the tops of old wooden poles are proving successful, suggesting that here too nesting sites were a limiting factor. The work in these two regions, however, appears to prove the exception rather than the general rule. Habitat loss is still without doubt the major cause of the bird's decline, but this should not inhibit the provision of artificial nest sites in regions where habitat is already good or is actively being restored.

Roads and traffic

Britain's road network has developed rapidly since the 1950s, and highways now cover more than 262,000 km (164,000 miles) with motorways and trunk roads now commonplace throughout most of urban and even rural Britain. Urbanization and the associated road development that it brings have been responsible for the disappearance of about 1,000,000 ha (8.5 per cent) of agricultural land over the last sixty years or so. Where motorways and other major roads have been built near new and expanding towns, this has undoubtedly put the nail in the coffin for many Barn Owl communities which were already under great pressure from the increasing level of human disturbance associated with development sprawl. This has contributed significantly to localized extinction on the outskirts of towns and cities. New and improved road networks, as well as causing direct loss of suitable farmland habitat (motorways consume upwards of 26 acres of farmland per mile), are probably more insidious because they disrupt the complex network of field, ditch and hedgerow patterns on more traditional farmland, which can in turn seriously fragment regions of prime Barn Owl habitat. This forces the birds to fly over the road in order to maintain the limits of their old home ranges, as well as tempting them to hunt low over the rough grassy verges which soon attract small-mammal communities. Both of these activities expose Barn Owls, perhaps more than any other bird to the hazards of fast-moving traffic, leading to what I estimate amounts to 3000–5000 deaths on Britain's roads every year.

Survey figures in the first half of the 1980s suggested that only twenty breeding pairs out of the 5000 pairs in Britain and Ireland were located within 1 km of any motorway and fewer than 100 pairs within 3 km, which for the majority of Barn Owls represents the maximum distance they would normally travel from the nest to hunt. A study of the M5 over the five-year period following its opening resulted in high levels of road mortality, involving forty notified casualties, found mainly during the winter and spring months of the first year. This motorway cuts through the Somerset Levels, an area famed for its high Barn Owl population in the early 1980s. By 1986, the number of dead Barn Owls being notified from this road had dropped to just two, and today very few casualties are now reported on the M5 in spite of a full-time researcher being present in the area who has made special efforts to encourage the police and the public to report all road victims from the M5. The declining numbers of road casualties can undoubtedly be attributed to the diminishing Barn Owl population, because the same researcher has found that the numbers of occupied breeding sites in the county of Avon together with the north-west region of the Somerset Levels has now fallen significantly since the survey was completed in 1985. While it cannot confidently be concluded that the M5 motorway has been the sole cause of the decline in the region, the facts clearly warrant further investigation. Elsewhere in the UK, where Barn Owls can still be found nesting close to motorways and dual carriageways, it may be significant that the roads involved are usually those which have only recently been constructed or improved and where perhaps existing Barn Owl communities are still in the process of being depleted.

Organochlorine pesticides

The devastating effects of environmentally persistent agricultural chemicals on non-target wildlife have featured prominently in the decline of many predatory birds which occupy a position at the top of the food chain (Newton 1979). The organochlorine pesticides, DDT, aldrin and dieldrin, were introduced in 1945 and 1955 to combat insect pests on standing crops such as cereals, brassicas and orchard fruits and soil pests such as wheat bulb fly, carrot fly and wireworms in potatoes.

The first confirmed Barn Owl casualty in the UK from one of these organochlorines was in 1960, and it was found that between 1967 and 1977 the Barn Owl was one of the species which had been contaminated, although it ranked only sixth in the bird-of-prey league table (Cook 1982). Following the more recent analysis of the tissues from specimens collected between 1963 and 1989, it was concluded that 56 of the 627 specimens analysed (9 per cent) probably died as a result of organochlorine pesticide poisoning and that 22 (40 per cent) of these 56 were from eastern counties of England (Newton et al. 1991). The first study had established that by 1971 Barn Owls were no longer showing major contamination from these chemicals, and recent specimens received and analysed between 1987 and 1989 in the study by Newton showed that they contained residues nowhere near the lethal dose. This indicated that the Barn Owl, like the Sparrowhawk, was no longer suffering any noticeable lethal or sublethal effects from these particular chemical contaminants.

Although the majority of raptors have recovered dramatically in response to falling levels of these environmental contaminants, the Barn Owl population in Britain and Ireland has, however, continued to decline, even though there has recently been some indication that more chicks have been raised to fledging from nests in eastern England since the 1970s (Percival 1990). Whether this is the result of a recovery from the pesticide contamination or reflects the increased number of nestboxes occupied, which has been a particular feature of this region since 1980, we shall never know, since Percival's preliminary work in 1988 also showed that nestboxes increase fledging success by up to 30 per cent because eggs seem to hatch more successfully in this situation. In addition, winters have been milder here since the 1970s, so making the reasons for any such trend difficult to interpret. When comparing this apparent recovery in eastern England with that of the Sparrowhawk, one of the most seriously contaminated raptors, there is little to cheer: Sparrowhawks were found in only three places during fieldwork for the first Hertfordshire Breeding Atlas between 1968 and 1972 (Mead and Smith 1982), but in 119 twenty years later during work for the new Atlas; Barn Owls, on the other hand, far from increasing over the last twenty years, have fallen from 33 proven pairs in the first Atlas to just six proven pairs today (Smith in press). Even if habitat loss or some other factor was at work here, some indication of a recovery over the last twenty years would have been anticipated if organochlorines were solely to blame in the 1960s. Likewise, even if the Barn Owl was lagging behind the Sparrowhawk in its return, we might have expected it to have demonstrated some increase over the last twenty years.

Rodenticides

A new and different class of pesticides used to kill rats and mice is now giving some cause for concern. These rodenticides, which were introduced in 1974, are known as 'second-generation' anticoagulants. The earlier 'first-generation compound', called warfarin and introduced in 1952, was based on the natural poisonous substance coumarin, found in clover hay. This anticoagulant acted by reducing the normal clotting enzymes so that the blood vessels continually leaked, and the rodent died through internal haemorrhaging one to three weeks after a lethal dose (which was usually presented on a suitable bait such as wheat grain). Warfarin had a fairly high safety margin for predatory birds such as the Barn Owl, which would need to consume twenty or more contaminated rodents, far in excess of its normal daily food requirement, to die from the secondary effects of poisoning. This wide safety margin seems to be confirmed by field studies in Malaysian oil-palm plantations, where Barn Owls regularly have the opportunity of preying on warfarin-contaminated rats without any noticeable mortality or changes in their breeding performance.

As early as 1958, rats were acquiring genetic resistance to warfarin, although in mice it had become countrywide by the 1960s. As a result the 'second-generation' anticoagulants were introduced in 1974, with a compound called difenacoum which had a potency about 100 times greater than warfarin. In 1980 a second compound, brodifacoum, was introduced, followed soon after by bromadiolone and in 1986 by flucomafen in Ireland, all of which had a somewhat higher potency than difenacoum. The high potency and in some cases greater persistence of some of these new anticoagulants in the tissues of animals indicated that as few as one to five contaminated rodents might now be sufficient to kill a wild Barn Owl. In 1985 brodifacoum poisoning in a wild Barn Owl was identified following postmortem examination and chemical analysis of its body tissues, and five

Barn Owls were listed among the various rodenticide victims examined between 1973 and 1986. These discoveries supported my own findings, when postmortem examination of twelve Barn Owls notified between 1982 and 1985 revealed extensive haemorrhaging, often on the breast or around the beak and cloaca, which could not reasonably be attributed to physical injury. Indeed, the reason these particular carcases were notified was that most were found with signs of blood and in some cases bruising on the breast. Most were found close to or within a farm building where a baiting programme with a 'second-generation' rodenticide had been carried out a week or more before the birds were found dead or dying (Shawyer 1985).

Rodent control in the UK is mainly confined to commensal rodents such as the Brown Rat and House Mouse in and around farm buildings or warehouses storing foodstuffs, but baiting does occur at the base of hedgerows, especially during late autumn and winter when rats begin moving to seek the shelter of farm buildings. Rodenticides are also commonly applied in in the field situation to protect game such as Pheasants from the ravages of rats and mice on grain hoppers. The use of rodenticides in the field exposes Barn Owls to a particular risk, since field margins are a primary hunting habitat for this species.

Difenacoum and bromadiolone have unrestricted use in Britain and are freely available to the public for agricultural and domestic use. Brodifacoum and flucomafen on the other hand, apart from experimental trials outdoors, are restricted by law to use within buildings and only by professional pest-controllers, although, as with other poisons they are misused. I have, for example, found brodifacoum being applied on two game-rearing estates in Hampshire and Norfolk both of which were close to a Barn Owl site.

The use of the more potent compounds, brodifacoum and flucomafen, even indoors, exposes the Barn Owl to a risk of secondary poisoning because it will commonly take refuge inside buildings in late autumn and in winter and feed on young rats and mice, particularly if winters are severe (when they depend more heavily on these small mammals for their overwintering survival). It has been argued that the exposure of Barn Owls to these chemicals is likely to be low, because the Brown Rat and House Mouse, although important components of the diet in Ireland (where the Field Vole and Common Shrew are absent), form only a small part of the Barn Owl's diet in Britain; but since in winter rats and mice are often confined in and around farm buildings, where Barn Owls are attracted, some contamination is likely. In addition, although rodenticides are targeted at commensal rodents, this does not mean that other small mammals are unaffected. When second-generation rodenticides are used around the outside of buildings, Wood Mice and voles can be attracted to the bait and become contaminated or fall victim to the poison. The Wood Mouse is an important secondary prey item for the Barn Owl, and may even be the primary prey in some parts of eastern and central England, making the Barn Owl's potential exposure to these rodenticides more likely.

The 'second-generation' rodenticides were originally used mainly where warfarin resistance was a problem, which would have confined any contamination of other wildlife to the resistant areas. Unlike warfarin, however, their increased potency meant that there was less need for prolonged baiting and this made them more cost-effective, which is one of the reasons why they have become widely used throughout many British farms in recent years.

Although a sudden decline in the Barn Owl population in an oil-palm estate in Malaysia was attributed to brodifacoum and another rodenticide, it is difficult to assess here in Britain, how many Barn Owls are affected by anticoagulants and whether or not the numbers involved are sufficient to influence their population.

Nevertheless, since 1985, detailed analytical work similar to that which identified the widespread exposure of birds of prey to the organochlorine pesticides has shown that a significant proportion of Barn Owl specimens received for chemical analysis, which were mainly the victims of road traffic or starvation, had detectable levels of brodifacoum and/or difenacoum within their liver tissue. Although this suggests fairly widespread contamination, the levels found were generally half those which would normally be expected to cause death or serious haemorrhage. It is not therefore possible to know whether these levels of contamination in wild owls would be sufficient to cause death, affect behaviour or influence breeding success. The fact that few specimens were received in circumstances suggesting they might have been poisoned does not necessarily indicate, however, that there is no problem, since it is likely that birds suffering from rodenticide poisoning would seek the confines of their roost and die unnoticed and would not be found.

A study of captive Barn Owls which had access to flucomafen has shown that its residues can be found in pellets, suggesting that this could be a suitable method of assessing the amount of direct exposure of Barn Owls to this rodenticide in the wild. Recent trials in Ireland, where Barn Owls feed more commonly on Brown Rats and where flucomafen is widely used, showed that none of the 89 pellets collected from wild owls contained detectable residues. However, it was accepted that more extensive population monitoring studies on Barn Owls could be valuable in areas where 'second-generation' anticoagulants are in regular use, and that this type of pellet-residue analysis may prove a useful technique.

Although organochlorines were responsible for the decline of many birds of prey, the effect of anticoagulants on the Barn Owl population in Britain and Ireland is still unknown.

14

CONSERVATION

There are obviously many factors which have to be taken into account in any strategy to conserve populations of the Barn Owl, including feeding habitat, nesting sites, climate, food supplementation, persecution, traffic and poisoning. A long-term conservation strategy for the Barn Owl was thus devised by the Hawk and Owl Trust which sought to protect and secure existing communities of this bird with a view to stabilizing the population and thereafter to expand it.

Measures

Since the Barn Owl population has declined largely because of major changes in agriculture which have led to a decline in its food supply, it follows that the most important conservation measures are the re-establishment of secure and uncontaminated feeding areas, as well as ensuring an adequate supply of undisturbed roosting and nesting opportunities. In many parts of Britain, pockets of good habitat still remain on some farms and estates. Yet even here Barn Owls have disappeared because their populations have been unable to survive in what have become discrete oases within an inhospitable landscape of intensively farmed or urbanized lands. For a conservation programme to succeed, therefore, it must also address this much larger issue of habitat fragmentation. Essentially this meant for the Hawk and Owl Trust a programme which could create rough grasslands in a way which could provide countrywide continuity for this owl from farm to farm and county to county (Brazil and Shawyer 1989).

My findings in the Lincolnshire fenlands, where the only available grasslands were along the banks of the rivers and drainage ditches, showed that Barn Owls were able to maintain high numbers over large areas in this intensively farmed county. It was clear, however, that they were present only in those regions and at those farms where the land was drained by rivers and ditches, suggesting that these microhabitats and the continuity they provided was critically important. My research indicated that 15–25 km of grassland edge 6 m wide or more appeared to be needed within a 1-km radius of the nest before Barn Owls would breed at the site.

As a consequence of these and other findings from elsewhere in Britain, a habitat-corridor scheme, the Farmland, Riverside and Forestry Link Initiative, was devised in 1989 as part of the Trust's new Barn Owl Conservation Network project. As the name suggests this national conservation programme focused attention on the re-establishment and better management of grassland and natural nesting sites found along natural features of the landscape, particularly the banks of rivers and ditches, field margins and woodland edge. The overall aim was to re-create habitat continuity and provide prey-rich corridors along which Barn Owls could feed and disperse successfully.

Once these margins have been created, either from scratch or by reducing the cutting frequency, they normally need little management but should be cut or grazed every third year or so in rotation. This prevents the complete shielding of light by the heavy litter layer, which can stagnate new grass growth. It also prevents invasion by scrub. Boundary posts, hedges or trees are important to the birds for 'still-hunting' along these grassy corridors, particularly during periods of snow cover, rain and high winds, and it is recommended that these are added at regular intervals of about 20 m or so along existing or newly created grassland.

This policy of maintaining and expanding existing Barn Owl communities in Britain is beginning to bear fruit. After ten years' work on private farmland in Galloway in Scotland, for example, the population in one study area has increased from forty to eighty pairs, about fifty of them regularly nesting in the nestboxes which have been provided; in this area, habitat quality was good but nesting sites were fast disappearing as old derelict cottages collapsed and others were renovated. In two other regions, one in the county of Avon the other in Bedfordshire, two grasslands were created from scratch and ample nestboxes supplied: Barn Owls began to colonize both of these two years after Field Voles became established, so that by the third year six breeding pairs were present, three of which produced double broods in their first year. These successes demonstrate the importance of applying the findings of the previous research and then testing them in the field. There is no doubt that Barn Owls are able to re-establish themselves quickly once the habitats are reinstated, and this programme, now underway on a countrywide basis, resulted in over 800 nestboxes being used in the UK in 1992 following habitat improvements.

Barn Owls are not the only species to benefit, and where these new habitats are already proving successful other species from insects to bats, as well as other small mammals, are flourishing once again. The Barn Owl is therefore an important flagship species for encouraging the creation of rough-grassland habitat.

Food in winter The Trust is currently undertaking trials to provide waste-grain dumps concealed within old straw bales around field headlands. High densities of small mammals have been found to congregate and breed in these during winter and, although they do not occur at the levels found in the much larger ricks of yesteryear, the provision of such dumps may prove a valuable conservation measure in winter. Some farmers traditionally provide dead mice caught in spring traps at Barn Owl winter roosts, and supplementary feeding with dead day-old cockerel chicks is not uncommon at some sites. This practice is not so simple as it sounds since the food rapidly chills and freezes, making it unacceptable to the owls, but with ingenuity and careful timing this can work successfully. In the Netherlands, supplementary feeding during severe winters is carried out routinely by an organized team of helpers who provide dead day-old cockerel chicks on heated stone bottles to try to maintain the country's

Hay and straw bales are the most commonly used nest site in farm buildings.

breeding population. However, it is rare for supplementary feeding of this type to be needed for extended periods. In Britain, the most severe snows and frosts occur during the months of January to March, and it is only during this time that artificial feeding is likely to become necessary.

Providing nestboxes It is a common misconception that the blanket provision of new nestboxes within a given region, or the erection of artificial sites in areas where Barn Owls are rare or unknown, will lead to new sites being taken up and an increase in the population. The widespread provision of boxes in the absence of firm knowledge of the local Barn Owl population can therefore be wasteful of resources and effort. However, this should never prevent nestboxes being erected in areas where suitable habitat is available or where it may provide an alternative site when a traditional one is under threat from development or decay. In fact, this is becoming increasingly important as more and more nesting sites are being lost, and my own studies now suggest that, where the bird's roosting sites are destroyed or subject to excessive human disturbance and there are no alternatives, Barn Owls will be lost from the area even though the main nesting site and foraging habitat remain largely unchanged. Nestboxes should therefore be erected to provide additional roosts where these are thought to be in short supply.

Nestboxes can also be very important at existing natural sites such as those in haystacks or strawstacks. These provide one of the most important breeding sites in the British Isles, constituting almost 40 per cent of those found in agricultural buildings. Although they are among the most secure and secluded of modern sites during the early part of the year, they soon

Hilary Burn

The provision of two-storey nest boxes has successfully encouraged Barn Owls back to areas where there was sufficient food but an insufficient supply of nest sites. The male can roost in the upper part of the box. Competition from Jackdaws, however, can cause problems both here and in natural sites.

become highly vulnerable as bales are removed during the spring, when eggs or young are often inadvertently destroyed (it seems that this is even more of a problem when spring is late and hay is consumed more rapidly because of the delayed growth of grass). During the Barn Owl Survey, over a half of these hay-bale sites were notified at the time the stacks were being dismantled, and it was estimated that about 450 pairs of Barn Owls would have failed as a result, which is almost 10 per cent of the estimated total population in Britain and Ireland. Clearly, because this is a very vulnerable nesting site, high priority must be given to ensuring its future security. More permanent sites such as nestboxes should be placed high in the roof space of hay barns, even though Barn Owls will sometimes continue to nest in the bale stack itself. Normally they can be encouraged to use the box if bales are piled up around it and the flight path into the entrance hole is unrestricted. Farmers sometimes construct tunnels and chambers between baless so that the entrance is clearly visible about two-thirds of the way up on an outside face of the stack. Often this wall of bales is left in place year after year so long as the chamber remains serviceable, while new bales are annually added to and consumed from the barn in the usual manner. The Hawk and Owl Trust provides details of a special box the size of a standard bale for this purpose. If nestboxes were provided and used by Barn Owls in these places, it is likely that an additional 1500 young Barn Owls would be produced in Britain and Ireland every year.

119

More young usually fledge from nestbox sites than from natural ones, and in the study in Scotland, where an equal number of artificial and natural sites are used, this has proved consitent over a number of years. The box locations may have been chosen originally because they appeared to offer prime habitat. When nestboxes are placed at existing natural sites more young fledge from them, probably as a result of the slightly lower mortality, since at some natural sites young fall off their breeding ledge regularly, perhaps because they are too cramped (the box was usually placed there because the natural site looked vulnerable). Whatever the reason, nestboxes do appear, in some cases at least, to increase the bird's overall productivity and may be useful for this reason alone.

Boxes are more commonly used for nesting if they are placed at or near known roosting sites. Often natural roosting sites in buildings do not offer a suitable nesting cavitity, and the provision of a box may attract the pair of owls if the existing site becomes unsuitable, or will encourage one of the offspring to pair up and nest in future years. Barn Owls sometimes return to a barn once it has been renovated if alternative sites were initially provided nearby. Soundproofed owl lofts can be successfully constructed in converted buildings when the entrance is at the more secluded end of the building, but the increased human disturbance which often accompanies these conversions into dwellings will often prevent the birds from returning.

Although in western districts buildings are the Barn Owl's favoured nest site, large cavities in isolated hedgerow or parkland trees are the preferred sites in eastern England, so it is important that old trees, especially those nearing the end of their natural life and considered by some to be in need of felling, are protected, since it is most commonly 300-year-old pollarded oaks or poorer rotted-out Ash that provide most of these tree sites today. Tree Preservation Orders (TPOs) rarely provide legal protection because there has so far not been any test case to confirm whether or not a TPO can be placed by virtue of fauna or flora it might contain, so protection is normally solely in the hands of the landowner or tenant farmer. Even old hollow stumps, the cavities of which have over time become exposed to the elements, can be prolonged if they are capped with a suitable board.

Nestboxes can be placed in trees, and many different designs from upright rectangular boxes to triangular ones are commonly used, but because of their immense size they are not always easy to erect. One of the main considerations should be to position the box entrance away from the prevailing wind but facing open land, so that the bird can locate the box easily and have a clear and unhindered flightpath into the box. An isolated parkland or hedgerow tree or one on the woodland edge overlooking open land are usually the only ones worth considering. I was once of the opinion that with tree boxes at least the entrance hole should be placed high up on the face of the box to prevent the young from falling out before they were ready. Recent work by Major Nigel Lewis, using image-intensifiers at night at occupied tree boxes with entrance holes at floor level, would indicate that this may not be necessary. These night observations have shown that young Barn Owls often fall out of boxes as they try to follow their older siblings who are nearing fledging, but that they are quite capable of walking their way up the trunk of the tree aided by rapid wing-flapping, when they usually go to the top of the box and regain entry by dropping down onto the landing ledge or the branch which is supporting the box. If the box protrudes beyond the side of the tree, however, this will prevent the birds returning successfully to the top of the box, and if they do they are able to get back inside only if a landing ledge has been provided for them to fall on to. Ideally, these boxes should be placed in substantial trees, cradled by an outgrowth of branches so that the young can return more easily. The crown of an ancient pollard is ideal, but where such trees are not available the box should have at least one sturdy branch around its base or alongside the entrance hole. Although boxes with high entrance holes may prevent the premature emergence of young owls, the box should still be positioned within a substantial tree cleft and have a landing ledge. In mature larch or spruce trees on the edges of commercial plantations, the box is usually strapped on to the main trunk. Because the branches occur in regular whorls up the trunk and around the box they offer more opportunity for the young birds to regain entry, but again it is always prudent to provide a substantial platform level with the base of the hole so that any inexperienced owls are able to regain entry into the box.

Caution should be exercised when siting these large and exposed tree boxes since they can attract unwanted human attention, particularly if they are located where the public has unrestricted access. They are therefore best sited on private farms and estates, rather than near footpaths or close to roads (which place the birds at an additional risk from traffic). As Barn Owls will nest in natural hollows in the tops of trees or within a hollow trunk at ground level, height is not a major consideration. The only consideration is the box's security from interference by man, and for this reason it is usually best to position it so that it can be reached only by ladder.

In some areas, although suitable foraging grounds can be created, natural structures do not exist for positioning nestboxes. In the Lincolnshire fenlands, the Hawk and Owl Trust began a major habitat-creation plan along two major river banks and ditchsides. Once the grasslands were in place and Barn Owls began to forage along them, there was an obvious need to provide artificial nest sites. One of the few options was to try positioning nestboxes on top of wooden poles. In Malaysia, the use of this type of box was pioneered by Dr Graham Lenton, and the Trust set about a scheme involving sixty boxes of similar design. These were two-chambered boxes with the upper, more exposed chamber under the pitched roof providing the opportunity for a separate roost for the male; this would allow the female to incubate and brood in the larger section below, within which a screen was placed to provide extra shelter from the severe winds experienced on the fenlands. Boxes were erected on poles in pairs, usually within 100 m of each other, and each pair was positioned 1 km apart.

These boxes have worked well, although the provision of two chambers has not yet been evaluated. In some instances, the male roosted in the box next to the nest rather than in the upper chamber of the same box, but, as anticipated, Kestrels found the more open chamber particularly attractive.

121

Avoiding disturbance Barn Owls are normally tolerant of a certain amount of disturbance, and many traditional sites can be found within busy modern farmyards. Those which are using a site for the first time, however, can be particularly sensitive and it is usually unwise to time visits when the birds are preparing to nest (during March) or in the early stages of incubation (in April and May) as this can lead to desertion of these new nests, particularly at exposed sites in trees or on poles.

Preventing mortality Drowning can be avoided by floating a plastic raft such as an old baking tray into cattle troughs, which allows cattle to drink while giving a Barn Owl a life raft and the means to escape. It is more difficult to tackle the problem of roads, but some success has been achieved by allowing hedges to grow high on roadsides where Barn Owls habitually cross; this forces them to fly higher above the road, thus avoiding with cars and lorries. The risks of poisoning can be reduced by careful use of products, following strictly the guidelines for their use.

Reintroduction Reintroduction of Barn Owls remains a controversial issue in Britain, arousing intense passion or conflict between academics and practitioners. Concerns relate to the possible competition with existing wild Barn Owls for limited food and nest sites when reintroduced birds are inadvertently placed in established territories. Other anxieties concern the risks of introducing disease into the existing wild population or releasing birds of inferior or unsuitable genetic stock. Both groups have valid arguments and neither has helped its cause: the practitioners because so few of them have monitored or recorded the outcome of their work and fail to understand that they should be aiming for a self-sustaining population, and the academics because they seem to have chosen to rely solely on theory.

Before embarking on any scheme, it is important to establish the root cause of the species' decline. If the major factor or factors can be identified and partially remedied, then subsequent reintroduction becomes a more rational choice. So far as the Barn Owl is concerned, this usually involves securing prey-rich habitats and sufficient additional roosting and nesting sites. Once these are established, the reintroduction methods used are varied but usually involve captive-breeding from permanently disabled but otherwise healthy wild adults. The offspring are then released, as fledglings or as adults, from a suitably modified and undisturbed farm building within prime habitat in the summer at a time when small-mammal numbers are increasing. Today, I estimate that about 1500 to 2000 Barn Owls are being released annually into the wild by about 400 operators, and the number of Barn Owls in captivity is now probably twice that in the wild.

The inescapable difficulty of Barn Owl reintroduction as a conservation initiative is that the level of mortality during the birds' first year of life appears to be similar to that of birds reared in the wild. In simple terms, this means that for every pair released there is a strong possibility that this partnership will not survive intact to breed in the following year, and the only way of giving this practice any chance of succeeding is for multiple releases to be undertaken within a carefully selected and controlled area.

The level of success seems directly related to this factor together with the degree of commitment of the practitioner and an understanding of the

Nest boxes should be designed and positioned in such a way that the young owls can successfully return to the box.

bird's ecology. Perhaps one of the best schemes operating in Britain is one in central England, where about ten pairs are now fully established, breeding every year as wild birds in an area where formerly there was none; its success has been due to the initial creation of large numbers of artificial nest sites within prime habitats. The scheme has received over sixty ringing records of dead birds which show that the causes of mortality are the same as those found in the wild, with no evidence of high levels of starvation. Different techniques have shown that adults that are released stay closer to the release site while young birds disperse 20 km or more, which is not unexpected since this is what tends to happen in the wild.

The Department of the Environment set up a working party in 1991 which examined the subject of reintroduction, and as a result the Barn Owl has been included on Schedule 9 of the Wildlife and Countryside Act 1981, which will encourage future reintroductions to be better controlled and coordinated and confined to licensed operators or licensed schemes. Reintroduction still needs a great deal more research and understanding before it can be considered as a necessary or worthy conservation practice in the Britain as a whole, but in capable hands it is able at the very least to achieve medium-term success in establishing self-sustaining communities where formerly they had been lost or had reached critical numbers.

With all the pressures on Britain's Barn Owl population it is going to take a long while and a great deal of conservation effort to bring it back to many of its former haunts. However, given prey-rich grasslands, spacious and secure nesting sites and freedom from human disturbance it is able to utilize its phenomenal breeding capability to bounce back from adversity.

Select Bibliography

Anderson, D.I.K, Petty, S.J., Little, B., and Davidson, M., 'Possible incestuous breeding by yearling Barn Owls *Tyto alba*', *The Naturalist* 991 (1989), 137–138

Batten, L., *Red Data Birds in Britain*, Poyser, Calton, 1990

Baudvin, H., 'Biologie de reproduction de la chouette effraie Tyto alba en Cote d'Or', *Premiers Resultants le Jean le Blanc* 14 (1975), 1–51

Blaker, G.B., *The Barn Owl in England and Wales*, RSPB, London, 1934

Brazil, M.A., and Shawyer, C.R., *The Barn Owl: The Farmer's Friend Needs a Helping Hand*, The Hawk Trust, London, 1989

Bunn, D.S., Warburton, A.B., and Wilson, R.D.S., *The Barn Owl*, Poyser, Calton,1982

Cayford, J, 'Barn Owl Ecology on East Anglian Farmland', RSPB Conservation Review 6 (1992), 45–50

Churchfield, S., *Shrews*, Nelson, Oswestry, 1986

Collinge, W.E., *The Food of Some British Wild Birds*, 1924-1927, privately published

Cramp, S., (Ed) *The Birds of the Western Palearctic*, IV, OUP, Oxford, 1985

Flowerdew, J., *Woodmice*, Nelson, Oswestry, 1984

Frank, F., 'The casualty of microtine cycles in Germany', *The Journal of Wildlife Management* 21 (1957), 113-121

Fussell, G.E., *Farming Technique from Prehistoric to Modern Times*, 1966

Gibbons, D.W., Reid, J.D. and Chapman, R.A., The New Atlas of Breeding Birds in Britain and Ireland 1988–1991, T. and A.D. Poyser, London, in press

Glue, D.E., 'Ringing recovery circumstances of small birds of prey', *Bird Study* 18 (1971), 137–46; 'Seasonal mortality in four small birds of prey', *Ornis*

Scandinavica 4 (1973), 97–102; 'Food of the Barn Owl in Britain and Ireland', *Bird Study* 21 (1974), 200–10

Hume, R., *Owls of the World*, Dragon's World, London, 1991

Jenkinson, R.D.S., and Gilbertson, D.D., *In the Shadow of Extinction*, Nottinghamshire and Derbyshire County Council, 1984

Johnson, P., 'Development of talon flange and serrations in the Barn Owl *Tyto alba* a guide to ageing', *Ringing and Migration* 12 (1991), 126–127

Lamb, H.H., 'Britain's changing climate' *The Biological Significance of Climatic Changes in Britain. Institute of Biology, Symposia 14*, Academic Press, London, 1965; 'Our changing climate' in Perring, F. (ed.), *The Flora of a Changing Britain*, Botanical Society of the British Isles, London, 1970

Langford, I.K., and Taylor, I.R., in Galbraith, C.A., Taylor, I.R., and Percival, S. (eds), *The ecology and conservation of European Owls*, 101–104, JNCC, Peterborough, 1993,

Lenton, G., 'Moult of Malayan Barn Owls *Tyto alba*', *Ibis* 126 (1984), 188–97; 'The feeding and breeding ecology of Barn Owls *Tyto alba* in Peninsular Malaysia', *Ibid.*, 551–75

Lewis, N., 'Buried Alive', *The Raptor* 19 (1992), 36

Mikkola, H., 'Owls killing and killed by other owls and raptors in Europe', *British Birds* 69 (1976), 144–54; *Owls of Europe*, Poyser, Calton, 1983

Newton, I., *Population Ecology of Raptors*, Poyser, Berkhamsted, 1979; *The Sparrowhawk*, Poyser, Calton, 1986

Newton, I., Wyllie, I., and Asher, A., 'Mortality Causes in British Barn Owls, *Tyto Alba*, with a discussion of aldrin and dieldrin poisoning', *Ibis* 133 (1991) 162–9

Pearce, G., 'Study of wild and released Barn Owls in east Devon, 1980–92', *Devon Birds* 45 (1992), 37–45

Percival, S., 'Populations trends in British Barn Owls, *Tyto alba*, and Tawny Owls, *Strix aluco*, in relation to environmental change' *BTO Research Report* 57 BTO, Tring, 1990

Piechocki, R., 'Über die Winterverluste bei Schleireulen *Tyto alba*' *Vogelwarte* 20 (1960), 274–80

Pollard, E., Hooper, M.D., and Moore, N.W., (eds), *Hedges*, Collins, London, 1974

Prestt, I., 'An enquiry into the recent breeding status of some of the smaller birds of prey and crows in Britain', *Bird Study* 12 (1965), 196–220

Sharrock, J.T.R., *The Atlas of Breeding Birds in Britain and Ireland*, BTO, Tring, 1976

Shaw, G., and Dowell, A., 'Breeding by closely related Barn Owls', *Ringing and Migration* 10:98 (1989), 98

Shawyer, C.R., *Rodenticides: A Review and Assessment of their Potential Hazard to Non-Target Wildlife with Special Reference to The Barn Owl* Tyto alba, The Hawk Trust, London, 1985; *The Barn Owl in the British Isles, its Past, Present and Future*, The Hawk Trust, London, 1987; 'Habitat requirements for Barn Owls', in Blossom, J. (ed.) *First National Barn Owl Conservation Network Symposium: The Future of Barn Owl Conservation in Britain and Ireland*, The Hawk Trust, London, 1988; in *Where to watch birds in Europe* , BirdLife International, Cambridge, 1993?

Shawyer, C.R., and Banks, P., 'An ill wind for Barn Owls', *BTO News* 155 (1988), 1, 4

Shrubb, M., *The Kestrel*, Hamlyn, London, 1993

Smal, C.M., 'The diet of the Barn Owl Tyto alba in southern Ireland, with reference to a recently introduced prey species – the Bank Vole *Clethrionomys glareolus*', *Bird Study* 34 (1987), 113–25

Snow, D.W., 'Movements and mortality of British Kestrels *Falco tinnunculus*', *Bird Study* 15 (1968), 65–83

Sparks, J., and Soper, A., *Owls*, David & Charles, London, 1970

Taylor, I.R., *The Barn Owl*, Shire Publications, Aylesbury, 1989

Ticehurst, C.B., 'On the food of the Barn Owl and its bearing on Barn Owl population', *Ibis* 5 (1935), 329–35

Twigg, G., *The Brown Rat*, David and Charles, Newton Abbot, 1975

Venables, L.S.V., and Leslie, P.H., 'The rat and mouse populations of corn ricks', *Journal of Animal Ecology* 11 (1942), 44–68

Village, A., *The Kestrel*, Poyser, London, 1990

Voous, K.H., *Owls of the Northern Hemisphere*, Collins, London, 1988

Witherby, H.F., Jourdain, F.C.R., Ticehurst, N.F., and Tucker, B.W., *The Handbook of Birds*, II, (Rev. Edn), Witherby, London, 1943

Scientific Names
of Species

BIRDS
Fulmar *Fulmarus glacialis*
Hammerkop *Scopus umbretta*
kites *Milvus* spp.
Hen Harrier *Circus cyaneus*
Goshawk *Accipiter gentilis*
Sparrowhawk *A. nisus*
Buzzard *Buteo buteo*
Osprey *Pandion haliaetus*
Kestrel *Falco tinnunculus*
Merlin *F. columbarius*
Peregrine *F. peregrinus*
Black Grouse *Tetrao tetrix*
Pheasant *Phasianus colchicus*
Whimbrel *Numenius phaeopus*
Redshank *Tringa totaus*
Greenshank *T. nebularia*
Barn Owl *Tyto alba*
Sula Islands Barn Owl *T. nigrobrunnea*
Great Horned Owl *Bubo virginianus*
Eagle Owl *B. bubo*
Snowy Owl *Nyctea scandiaca*
Little Owl *Athene noctua*
Tawny Owl *Strix aluco*
Great Grey Owl *S. nebularia*
Long-eared Owl *Asio otus*
Short-eared Owl *A. flammeus*
Nightjar *Caprimulgus europaeus*
Meadow Pipit *Anthus pratensis*
Magpie *Pica pica*
Jackdaw *Corvus monedula*
Carrion Crow *C. corone*
Starling *Sturnus vulgaris*
House Sparrow *Passer domesticus*
finches *Fringillidae*
buntings *Emberizinae*

MAMMALS
Mole *Talpa europaea*
Common Shrew *Sorex araneus*
Pygmy Shrew *S. minutus*
Water Shrew *Neomys fodiens*
Rabbit *Oryctolagus cuniculus*
Grey Squirrel *Sciurus carolinensis*
Arctic Lemming *Dicrostonyx torquatus*
Bank Vole *Clethrionomys glareolus*
Field/Short-tailed Vole *Microtus agrestis*
Common Vole *M. arvalis*
Root Vole *M. oeconomus*
Gregarious Vole *M. gregalis*
Water Vole *Arvicola terrestris*
Brown Rat *Rattus norvegicus*
Wood Mouse *Apodemus sylvaticus*
Harvest Mouse *Micromys minutus*
House Mouse *Mus musculus*
Stoat *Mustela erminea*
Weasel *M. nivalis*
Mink (American) *M. vison*
Pine Marten *Martes martes*

PLANTS
Ash *Fraxinus excelsior*
beech *Fagus* spp.
Elm (English) *Ulmus procera*
Cornish Elm *U. angustifolia*
Small-leaved Elm *U. carpinifolia*
Oak (Pedunculate) *Quercus robur*
Norway Spruce *Picea abies*
Sitka Spruce *P. sitchensis*
willow *Salix* spp.
Brown Bent *Agrostis canina*
Cock's-foot *Dactylis glomerata*
False Oat-grass *Arrhenatherum elatius*
Fiorin Grass *Agrostis palustris*
Meadow Fescue *Festuca elatior*
Meadow Foxtail *Alopecurus pratensis*
Meadow Soft-grass (Yorkshire-fog) *Holcus lanatus*
Slender False Brome *Brachypodium sylvaticum*

Index

References in *italics* are to illustrations.

afforestation, effects of 29
ageing 19–20
aggression 58, 64–5, 69
Agricultural Research Council 24
agriculture, effects of 22–5,
   31–2, 102–104, 105–107
allopreening 70

bigamy 80
bill 10, 13
breeding 67–87
  age of first 68
  density 58–9
  failure 80–81
  success 71–2, 73–6, 81, 84–5,
   93
British Trust for Ornithology 93

calls 61–3, 65–6, 69, 70, 75, 76
camouflage 12, 13
classification 10–11
claws 15
climate, effects of 25, 26–8,
   29–30, 31, 85–7, 102–105
clutch size 67, 71–2
conservation 28, 115–123
copulation 62, 70
courtship 67, 68–70
  feeding 69–70, 72
  flights 68–9

death, causes of 18, 19, 38,
   94–114
defence 63, 65–6, 77
deforestation, effects of 21–2,
   102
description 10, 12–20
digestion 56–7
dimorphism, sexual 12, 17–19
dispersal, juvenile 27, 28, 91

display 65–6
distribution 10–11, 21, 22,
   26–34, *11*
droppings 55, 76

ears 10, 15–16
eggs 67, 71–2
eyes 10, 16–17, 76, 77

feet 13–15
fledging 67, 78
  success 67
flight 50–51
food
  competition for 92–3, 100–101
  nutritional requirements
   18–19, 43, 48–50, 67–8, 70,
   72–3, 76, 77, 78–9, 81–4, 93
  shortages, temporary, effect on
   plumage of young 20

gamekeeping, effects of 24–5

habitat 11, 13, 21–5, 32, 35–42,
   58
  destruction 107–111
hatching 67, 73–6
  asynchronous 67, 71, 73
history 21–5
hunting techniques 50–54

incest 79–80
incubation 71, 72–3
Institute of Terrestrial Ecology
   19, 20, 94

legs 10, 13–14
lifespan 92–3

mortality 18, 19, 38, 93–114

seasonal 98
moult 12, 20, 88–90

names 11
nestboxes 59, 101, 117–122
nesting 71
  communal 59
nest site 37–42, 65
  competition 68, 101
  fidelity 59, 68, 79–80, 91
  selection 37–42

oviducts 20
owls, classification 10
Owl, Great Grey 85
Owl, Little 65
Owl, Long-eared 15, 17
Owl, Short-eared 15, 17, 45
Owl, Tawny 15, 18, 19, 21, 25,
  31, 58, 59, 68

pair-bond 68
parasitism by other species 52,
  65
pellets 43, 54–6, 57, 76
persecution 22, 24–5, 27, 97
pesticides 31–2, 97–8, 111–114
plumage 10, 12–13, 19–20, 51,
  88–90
  of chicks 76, 77, 90
  of juveniles 12, 19–20, 90
  sexual dimorphism 12, 19
populations 24–5, 26–34, 58–9,
  92–3, 102–4
  fluctuations 29–31, 48, 59,
  84–5

predators 66, 99–101
prey
  size 43–5
  species 21, 22, 24, 37
protection, legal 25, 33–4, 123

races 10–11, 26
range
  home 36, 50, 58–9
  hunting 36, 58, 60
  roosting sites 42, 60, 72–3

second broods 80–81
sexing 19–20
sight 16–17
size 12, 17
survey, 1932 28–30, 33
survey 1982–5 28, 32 ff., 94

talon flange 20
territory 58

voice 61–3
vole cycle 29, 32, 48, 59, 84–5

weather, effects of 20, 26–8, 29,
  31, 36–8, 53–4, 60, 71, 80,
  85–7
weight 10, 17–19, 95
  fluctuations in 18–19, 48–50,
  70, 76–8
  sexual dimorphism 17, 18, 19
wings 10, 12–13

young, development of 76–7